OXFORD
UNIVERSITY PRESS

Janet Hardy-Gould
Kate Mellersh

English Plus

Workbook 2

UNIVERSITY PRESS

Great Clarendon Street, Oxford OX2 6DP

Oxford University Press is a department of the University of Oxford.
It furthers the University's objective of excellence in research, scholarship,
and education by publishing worldwide in

Oxford New York

Auckland Cape Town Dar es Salaam Hong Kong Karachi
Kuala Lumpur Madrid Melbourne Mexico City Nairobi
New Delhi Shanghai Taipei Toronto

With offices in

Argentina Austria Brazil Chile Czech Republic France Greece
Guatemala Hungary Italy Japan Poland Portugal Singapore
South Korea Switzerland Thailand Turkey Ukraine Vietnam

OXFORD and OXFORD ENGLISH are registered trade marks of
Oxford University Press in the UK and in certain other countries

ISBN: 978 0 19 474861 2   Workbook
ISBN: 978 0 19 474885 8   MultiROM
ISBN: 978 0 19 474877 3   Pack

Printed in China

This book is printed on paper from certified and well-managed sources.

ACKNOWLEDGEMENTS

Illustrations by: Paul Daviz p.4, 9, 16, 19; Peter Ellis/Meiklejohn pp.8, 24, 26,
56; Martina Farrow 17, 29, 33, 58, 96, 97, 99; David Oakley p.94, 95, 98; Andy
Parker p.34.

Cover photographs: Photolibrary (Rafting/Glow Images, Couple taking
photograph/Photodisc/White, Teen girls doing homework/Andersen Ross/
White); PunchStock (University students on campus/moodboard).

*The publisher would like to thank the following for their permission to reproduce
photographs*: Alamy Images pp.10 (Girl playing guitar/Catchlight Visual
Services), 12 (Man in house/Janine Wiedel Photolibrary), 16 (Seafront
apartments/Gregory Davies), 34 (Beach/Images of Africa Photobank), 37 (Isle
of Wight/nobelIMAGES), 55 (exam/Jim Wileman), 66 (Thailand/Robert
Harding Picture Library Ltd); Collections p.20 (Houseboat/Keith Pritchard);
Corbis pp.15 (Girl using laptop/Jim Craigmyle), 40 (Cristiano Ronaldo/
Matthew Ashton/AMA), 40 (Agatha Christie/Bettmann), 42 (Blue whale/Denis
Scott), 45 (Harry Potter cast members/Luke Macgregor/Reuters), 50 (Teen
girl with braces/Ken Weingart); Famous p.40 (Leona Lewis); Getty Images
pp.21 (Miley Cyrus tour bus/WireImage), 40 (Russian ballet dancer Mikhail
Barishnikov/Popperfoto), 40 (J S Bach/Archive Photos), 40 (Engraved Portrait
Of Michelangelo), 45 (Michael Jackson/Redferns), 47 (Leonardo DiCaprio/
Michel Loccisano), 60 (Table tennis player Paul Drinkhall), 69 (TV camera crew
report in a flooded street); iStockphoto pp.7 (High school student/Hongqi
Zhang), 31 (Graduation/Sean Locke), 42 (Dolphins/Tom Hirtreiter); Nature
Picture Library pp.28 (Clark's Nutcracker/George McCarthy), 42 (Rabbits/Terry
Andrewartha); Oxford University Press pp.5 (Man holding CD/Photodisc),
6 (Boy doing science experiment/Image Source), 8 (Boy with MP3 player/
Stockbyte), 13 (Teen boy/Image Source), 18 (Teenager vacuuming bedroom/
Photodisc), 29 (Tower Bridge/Digital Vision), 31 (teenagers/PhotoAlto),
42 (Tigers running along beach/Flame/DLILLC), 42 (White terrier dog/Digital
Vision), 44 (Portrait of teen boy/Blend Images), 44 (Girl studying at home/
Comstock), 50 (Smiling teen boy/Pixland), 64 (Boy with backpack/Imageshop);
Photolibrary p.71 (Tennis player with injured knee/Comstock); Press
Association Images pp.27 (Florence Nightingale/PA Archive), 28 (Chimpanzee
doing memory test/Tetsuro Matsuzawa/AP), 36 (*The Long Way Down*/Jerome
Delay/AP), 42 (Chimpanzee memory test/Tetsuro Matsuzawa/AP), 52 (Tiger
Woods/Charlie Riedel/AP), 59 (Rafael Nadal/Grant Treeby/World Sports
Pictures), 65 (Laura Robson/PA Wire/PA Archive); Rex Features pp.49 (Tom
Cruise and Katie Holmes/Julian Makey), 68 (Oblivion rollercoaster/Sonny
Meddle); The Times p.32 (Motorcyclist jumping buses/Chris Bromham).

*Although every effort has been made to trace and contact copyright holders before
publication, this has not been possible in some cases. We apologise for any apparent
infringement of copyright and, if notified, the publisher will be pleased to rectify any
errors or omissions at the earliest possible opportunity.*

Contents

VOCABULARY ▪ Family

1 ★ Match words 1–6 with the words in the box.

> sister   mother   niece   ~~daughter~~   wife
> granddaughter   aunt

son __daughter__

1 nephew _____
2 uncle _____
3 father _____
4 husband _____
5 brother _____
6 grandson _____

2 ★ Complete the sentences with the words in exercise 1.

My aunt's __husband__ is my uncle.

1 My sister is my father's _____.
2 My mother's _____ is my father.
3 My father's brother is my _____.
4 My aunt's _____ is my brother.
5 My father's _____ is my mother.
6 My mother's _____ is my aunt.

3 ★★ Read the sentences about famous families. Choose the correct answers.

Singer Dannii Minogue is Kylie Minogue's
sister .

   a child   b daughter   c (sister)   d cousin

1 Bart Simpson is Lisa's ___.
   a brother   b son   c father   d nephew
2 Luke Skywalker in *Star Wars* is
  Darth Vader's ___.
   a cousin   b brother   c son   d uncle
3 Singer Vanessa Paradis is Johnny Depp's ___.
   a niece   b aunt   c partner
   d grandmother
4 James and Oliver Phelps are ___ Fred and
  George Weasley in the *Harry Potter* films.
   a twins   b cousins   c sons
   d grandparents
5 Katie Holmes and Tom Cruise's ___ is a little
  girl called Suri.
   a son   b brother   c daughter   d father
6 Lourdes, Rocco, David and Mercy are
  Madonna's ___.
   a sons   b nieces   c nephews   d children

4 ★★ Complete the sentences.

Joseph married to Grace

Mark married to Clare   Emma married to David

Oliver   Daniel   Laura

Mark is Clare's __husband__ .

1 Joseph and Grace are Oliver's _____.
2 Joseph and Grace are Mark and Emma's
  _____.
3 Mark and Emma are Joseph and Grace's
  _____.
4 David is Oliver's _____.
5 Clare is Daniel and Laura's _____.
6 Daniel is Mark's _____.
7 Laura is Mark's _____.
8 Daniel and Oliver are _____.
9 Laura is Joseph and Grace's _____.
10 Daniel is Joseph and Grace's _____.

5 ★★★ Write sentences about your family. Use some of the words in the box.

> his / her   married to   wife   our
> nephew(s) / niece(s)   child(ren)   twins
> cousin(s)   my   aunt / uncle

My aunt's name is Carolina.

1 _____
2 _____
3 _____
4 _____
5 _____
6 _____

be + subject pronouns

1 ⭐ Complete the tables with the words in the box.

> 's   not   're   aren't   ~~'m~~   isn't

Affirmative		
Subject pronoun	**be**	**Other words**
I	'm	15 years old.
He / She / It	1 _____	from London.
We / You / They	2 _____	Harry's cousin(s).

Affirmative	Negative	Question	Answer
I'm	I'm 3 _____	Am I … ?	Yes, you are. / No, you aren't.
He's	He 4 _____	Is he … ?	Yes, he is. / No, he isn't.
They're	They 5 _____	Are they … ?	Yes, they are. / No, they aren't.

2 ⭐⭐ Complete the sentences with the correct subject pronoun.

This is Marina. __She__ 's Italian.

1 Martin and I are German. _____'re from Hamburg.
2 Emily and Kate aren't here. _____'re at the cinema.
3 Are you Hungarian?
   Yes, _____ am.
4 I've got a new book. _____'s very interesting.
5 That's my dad. _____'s a maths teacher.
6 Am I late?
   No, _____ aren't.

3 ⭐⭐ Complete the sentences about famous places with the affirmative or negative form of *be*.

Wembley stadium __isn't__ in Berlin.

1 Kraków _____ in Poland.
2 Buckingham Palace and Big Ben _____ in Lisbon.
3 The White House _____ in Canada.
4 Beijing and Shanghai _____ in China.
5 The Eiffel Tower _____ in Paris.
6 The Taj Mahal _____ in India.
7 Prague and Vienna _____ in Russia.
8 The Colosseum _____ in London.

4 ⭐⭐⭐ Use words from the table to write six questions. Then write answers that are true for you.

What How old Who When Where	is / 's are / 're	your favourite food? your school? your best friends? your next holiday? your favourite actors? your mother's birthday? your favourite colour?

What's your favourite food? It's pizza.

1 _____
2 _____
3 _____
4 _____
5 _____
6 _____

Possessive *'s*

5 ⭐⭐ Correct the sentences. Put the apostrophe in the correct place.

This is Marks CD.
__Mark's__

1 Where are Peters shoes? _____
2 My parents car is white. _____
3 My English teachers house is near the school. _____
4 My brothers names are Josh and Adam. _____
5 This is James and Saras cousin. _____
6 My grandparents house is in France. _____

6 ⭐⭐⭐ Look again at the family tree on page 4. Write sentences.

Daniel / Joseph and Grace
__Daniel is Joseph and Grace's grandson.__

1 Daniel and Laura / Oliver
_____

2 Oliver / Emma
_____

3 Mark and Emma / Joseph
_____

4 Laura / David and Emma
_____

5 Clare / Daniel

VOCABULARY ■ School

1 ★ Complete the words in the sentences.

I don't understand my m<u>aths</u> homework!

1 We've got a lesson in the s_____ laboratory.

2 We're on page ten of our g_____ book. It's all about Africa.

3 My P_____ teacher teaches football and basketball.

4 At school there's a m_____ room with a piano.

5 This E_____ exercise isn't difficult. All the words are on this page.

6 My next c_____ is in room 15. It's at ten o'clock.

2 ★★ Complete the sentences with the words in the box.

> book   notes   exam   room   ~~laboratory~~
> teacher   homework

My brother's school has got a new science ___laboratory___ .

1 Listen and write _____ about the British Royal Family.

2 We've got an English _____ on Monday.

3 Open your history _____ at page fifty-nine.

4 Our PE _____ is very good at basketball.

5 We've got a lot of French _____ today – four exercises!

6 Where's our next lesson? It's in the ICT _____ .

3 ★★ Read the notes and complete the dialogue.

Monday
Important! Shorts and T-shirt for PE class.

Tuesday
Geography homework and science homework.

Wednesday
music lesson – remember book!

Thursday
9.00 a.m. Exam – history.

Friday
~~maths homework:~~

Lily   I've got a lot to do this week. I've got ___science___ and ¹_____ homework on Tuesday.

Mum   Have you? Have you got any more?

Lily   No. We haven't got ²_____ homework on Friday, because we're on holiday next week.

Mum   Oh, yes. That's good.

Lily   But I've got a history ³_____ on Thursday.

Mum   Oh, no! Really?

Lily   And I need my music ⁴_____ for Wednesday. I've got a lesson.

Mum   Yes, I know.

Lily   And there's a PE ⁵_____ on Monday. I need my shorts and T-shirt!

4 ★★★ Answer the questions. Write true sentences.

What homework have you got this week?
I've got French homework.

1 What exams have you got before the holidays?
_____

2 What books have you got in your school bag?
_____

3 What are your favourite lessons?
_____

4 How many teachers have you got?
_____

5 Have you got an ICT room?
_____

6 Who is your favourite teacher?
_____

have got

1 ⭐ Complete the table with the words in the box.

~~have~~ has haven't hasn't have

	I / you / we / they	he / she / it
Affirmative	I / you / we / they <u>have</u> got	he / she / it has got
Negative	I / you / we / they haven't got	he / she / it ³_____ got
Question	¹_____ they got...?	Has it got...?
Answers	Yes, they have. No, they ²_____.	Yes, it ⁴_____. No, it hasn't.

2 ⭐⭐ Complete the sentences with the correct form of *have got*.

<u>Have we got</u> (we) a new English teacher this year?

1 They're very happy. They _____ homework tonight.

2 My cousin is interested in music and he _____ a guitar.

3 You _____ a history lesson today. It's on Friday.

4 _____ (the teacher) a new science book?

5 What exercises _____ (you) for your maths homework?

6 Where _____ (she) her history lesson?

3 ⭐⭐ Write questions with *have got*. Complete answers a–e. Then match questions 1–5 with answers a–e.

1 you / a strict teacher?
<u>Have you got a strict teacher?</u> <u>a</u>

2 your brother / a maths exam on Friday?
_____ __

3 we / two exercises for homework?
_____ __

4 the school / a new science laboratory?
_____ __

5 they / an interesting geography book?
_____ __

a No, I <u>haven't</u>. She's very nice.
b Yes, they _____. It's about mountains.
c No, we _____. We've got three.
d No, it _____. It's got a new music room.
e Yes, he _____. He isn't very happy.

there is, there are

4 ⭐⭐ Complete the text with *there is, there isn't, there are* or *there aren't*.

My school

My name's Adam and I'm at Priory School in Manchester. Priory is a small school – <u>there are</u> only two hundred students here. It's a school for boys, so ¹_____ any girls. ²_____ twenty or thirty teachers at the school and ³_____ a lot of different rooms.

I'm interested in sport and ⁴_____ a big gymnasium for our PE classes – that's important for me! ⁵_____ also two excellent PE teachers, Mr Bailey and Mr Stratton, but ⁶_____ a swimming pool here at Priory School – we go to the city centre for swimming classes.

I love science and ⁷_____ a big new science laboratory. I like ICT too, but ⁸_____ any modern computers in our ICT room. They're very old!

5 ⭐⭐⭐ Write sentences about your school. Use the correct forms of *have got* and *there is / there are* and the words in the box. Use the text in exercise 4 to help you.

students teachers swimming pool
rooms school uniform gymnasium
computers laboratory

<u>We've got a blue and black school uniform.</u>

<u>There are seven hundred students at my school.</u>

1 _____
2 _____
3 _____
4 _____
5 _____
6 _____

1 □□□□□□□□ Possessions

VOCABULARY ■ Everyday objects

1 ★ Choose the odd word out.

clothes (keys) jewellery make-up

1 money a purse keys a wallet
2 a ticket a bus pass make-up an ID card
3 a purse a laptop a mobile phone an MP3 player
4 a key ring a watch sunglasses clothes
5 a purse a bag a wallet jewellery

2 ★★ Complete the sentences with the words in the box.

> keys bus pass make-up watch
> ID card mobile phone ~~laptop~~ money
> MP3 player

You can do work on your _laptop_.

1 You use a _____ to tell the time.
2 You put _____ in a purse.
3 I don't need a ticket for the bus. I've got a _____.
4 You can listen to music on an _____.
5 You can text friends on a _____.
6 Laura never wears _____ at school.
7 I can't open the door because I haven't got my _____.
8 We need an electronic _____ to go into school.

3 ★★ Look at the pictures. What do the people need? Complete the sentences.

The girl needs some more ___clothes___.

1 The boys need a _____.

2 The woman needs her _____.

3 The man needs his _____.

4 The girl needs a _____.

5 The boys need their _____.

4 ★★★ Write sentences about the objects you carry. Why do you carry them? Give reasons with *so*.

I carry a mobile phone so I can text my friends.

1 _____
2 _____
3 _____
4 _____
5 _____
6 _____

1 ⭐ Complete the table with the words in the box.

~~like~~   don't   like   likes   doesn't

Present simple affirmative		
I / You / We / They	<u>like</u>	pizza.
He / She / It	1_____	
Present simple negative		
I / You / We / They	2_____	4_____ pizza.
He / She / It	3_____	

2 ⭐⭐ Write negative sentences.

Clara wears jewellery.
<u>Clara doesn't wear jewellery.</u>

1 He buys a lot of designer clothes.
_____

2 They work in town.
_____

3 Frank studies a lot.
_____

4 We like hip hop music.
_____

5 She carries an ID card.
_____

6 My dog needs a drink of water.
_____

3 ⭐⭐ Write sentences using the present simple.

school / finish / at three o'clock
<u>School finishes at three o'clock.</u>

1 he / not carry / any money
_____

2 she / watch / too much TV
_____

3 he / go / swimming twice a week
_____

4 we / not like / horror films
_____

5 she / not wear / make-up
_____

6 he / use / an MP3 player to listen to music
_____

4 ⭐⭐⭐ Look at the pictures. Complete the sentences using the present simple affirmative and negative.

<u>She doesn't wear</u>
a lot of jewellery.

1 _____
to school by bus.

2 _____
football on
Saturdays.

3 _____
TV in the evenings.

4 _____
Chinese on Monday
nights.

5 _____
to the cinema with
her friends.

VOCABULARY ■ Free-time activities

1 ⭐ Complete the crossword.

R
E
A
D

read magazines / books

1 _____ TV
2 _____ sport
3 _____ music / the radio
4 _____ photos
5 _____ friends
6 _____ the internet
7 _____ things / tickets
8 _____ shopping / cycling

2 ⭐⭐ Complete the sentences with the verbs in exercise 1.

I often _meet_ Tim for coffee after school.

1 Mike _____ tennis very well.
2 Hayley and her sister _____ old cinema tickets. They've got about 25!
3 Sasha _____ shopping with her friends on Saturdays.
4 We _____ photos in our spare time.
5 Yen _____ computer magazines.
6 My brothers _____ the internet every day.

3 ⭐⭐ Complete Ana's description of her family. Use the verbs in the box.

> reads   don't watch   goes   doesn't go
> surf   ~~takes~~   listen to   play

The people in my family have got lots of interests. My dad really likes photography. He _takes_ photos at weekends, and he's in a photography club, too. He also ¹_____ swimming, but he ²_____ cycling. He says it's boring. My mum ³_____ magazines in the evening, and I ⁴_____ the guitar. She and I ⁵_____ the radio a lot, but we don't like the same music! I ⁶_____ TV very much, because I think the programmes are terrible. But I ⁷_____ the internet every night, and talk to my friends online.

4 ⭐⭐⭐ Complete the sentences about you and your friends' free time. Use affirmative and negative forms of suitable verbs and add your own ideas.

My dad _reads sports and photography magazines._ (magazines)

1 I _____
   _____.
   (TV / DVDs)
2 My best friend _____
   _____.
   (shopping at weekends)
3 My friends and I _____
   _____.
   (the guitar)
4 In our family, we _____
   _____.
   (the internet)
5 My best friend _____
   _____.
   (cycling)
6 I _____
   _____.
   (the radio)

Present simple: questions

1 ⭐ Look at the table. Choose the correct words.

Questions			
Do / Does	**Subject**	**Verb**	**Other words**
(Do) / Does	you	¹**play / plays**	tennis at the weekend?
²**Do / Does**	Sarah	³**surf / surfs**	the internet in the evening?

Short answers
Yes, I ⁴**do / does / am.** No, I ⁵**don't / doesn't / am not.**
Yes, she ⁶**do / does / is.** No, she ⁷**don't / doesn't / not.**

2 ⭐ Complete the sentences with *do* or *does*.

<u>Do</u> you use your mobile phone a lot?
1 Where _____ Millie and Claire go shopping?
2 When _____ we finish school?
3 _____ you read manga comics?
4 What _____ Jack collect?
5 _____ Kelly spend a lot of time watching TV?
6 Who _____ you play sport with?

3 ⭐⭐ Order the words to make present simple questions. Then match questions 1–5 with answers a–f.

tennis / you / when / play / do
<u>When do you play tennis?</u> _____ *e*
1 he / after school / does / visit / who

_____ __
2 do / live / they / where

_____ __
3 study / does / she / French

_____ __
4 they / do / go swimming / why / before school

_____ __
5 you / do / the internet / surf / why

_____ __

a No, she studies Spanish.
b In a flat near the city centre.
c He visits his grandmother.
d So I can watch videos and visit chat rooms.
e I play on Sundays.
f Because they want to be Olympic swimmers.

4 ⭐⭐⭐ Write questions for the answers. Look at the <u>underlined</u> words and use the correct words in the box. Then write true answers.

~~what~~   what   when   where   who   why

<u>What sports do you play?</u>
I play <u>tennis</u>.
<u>I play football and cricket.</u>
1 _____
I meet my friends <u>in town</u>.
_____
2 _____
I <u>read magazines and books</u> at the weekend.
_____
3 _____
I go shopping <u>on Saturdays</u>.
_____
4 _____
I like to go cycling with <u>my brother</u>.
_____
5 _____
I study English <u>because I want to visit Scotland</u>.
_____

Adverbs of frequency

5 ⭐⭐ Rewrite the sentences. Put the adverbs of frequency in the correct places.

I wear jewellery. (sometimes)
<u>I sometimes wear jewellery.</u>
1 We are tired in the evenings. (usually)
_____
2 Eva wears too much make-up. (often)
_____
3 Roberto sees his family. (hardly ever)
_____
4 I have got my ID card in my wallet. (always)
_____
_____
5 Laura is late for school. (never)
_____
6 They visit us at the weekend. (sometimes)
_____
_____

1 ★ Read the text. Tick ✔ the correct box.

The text is about …

a ☐ a typical London lifestyle.
b ☐ an expensive lifestyle.
c ☐ living without money.

A free and easy life

A

For many people, life is about working and having a lot of money and possessions. Without these things, your life isn't supposed to be very good. Some people disagree, however. Paul Cortez is one young person who lives an 'alternative lifestyle'.

B

Paul lives in a very expensive city, London, but he doesn't mind not having money. He stays in a squat*. It's not his home and he doesn't pay rent money. In many countries, this is not allowed, but in the UK, it's not illegal. He normally spends less than £1 a day.

C

Paul doesn't use public transport, and he hasn't got a car. He always rides a bicycle. 'It's cold in the winter, but I prefer it,' he says.

D

Paul doesn't have a paid job, but he's not bored. He is allowed to study very cheaply, because he hasn't got a job. He also works at a charity shop. He meets some fascinating people there.

E

Paul says that local cafés and supermarkets throw away a lot of good food, and he eats this. On a typical day, he has sandwiches and fresh fruit. Does he miss his favourite foods and drinks? 'Well, a really good coffee, maybe!' he says.

*squat – a squat is a home with squatters in it. A squatter lives in somebody else's home, without permission, and without paying any money. You can do this in the UK, until the home owner tells you to leave.

2 ★★ Read the text again. Match questions 1–4 with paragraphs A–E.

What do we want from life?	A
1 How does he travel?	—
2 What about food?	—
3 How does he do it?	—
4 What does he do all day?	—

3 ★★★ Answer the questions. Write complete sentences.

1 How is Paul Cortez's lifestyle 'alternative'?
_____

2 What city does he live in?
_____

3 How does he feel about having no money?
_____

4 What does he dislike about riding a bicycle?
_____

5 What activities does Paul do?
_____

6 Where does Paul get his food?
_____

Build your vocabulary

4 ★★ Complete the sentences with the words in the box.

> against the rules   aren't   allowed to
> is supposed   are allowed   supposed

1 We're _____ wear jewellery at school.

2 It's _____ to wear jewellery at school.

3 You aren't _____ to eat in class.

4 He _____ to wear a tie to school.

5 We _____ to use a mobile phone here.

6 We _____ supposed to make calls.

Language point: Capital letters and punctuation

1 ⭐ Choose the correct words.

Keiko is (Japanese) / japanese.

1 Their favourite group is *black eyed peas* / *Black Eyed Peas*.
2 Hes / **He's** got a cat.
3 **It's** / Its eyes are blue.
4 I'm into **music art and, reading** / **music, art and reading**.
5 We went to **Spain** / spain last summer.
6 do / **Do** you like hip hop music?
7 I want to learn **Spanish Japanese and French** / **Spanish, Japanese and French**.
8 She is **Australian** / australian.

2 ⭐⭐ Rewrite the sentences using capital letters and punctuation.

my name is laura and ive got a lot of comics books and magazines

<u>My name is Laura and I've got a lot of comics,</u>

<u>books and magazines.</u>

1 im really into them i also like playing my brother jamess computer games he doesnt mind

_____

_____

2 we like art reading and playing football were into music too

_____

_____

3 weve got about 100 cds theyre on shelves in our bedroom

_____

_____

○ TASK

3 ⭐⭐ Read the information about Rasheed and complete the description.

Name: Rasheed

Age: 14

Description: quiet, friendly

Likes: football ✔, volleyball ✔, shopping ✘

Habits: plays football and reads manga comics

Buys: football magazines

Wants to meet: somebody aged 14–16

Speaks: English, Spanish and French

Wants to learn: German and how to play the guitar

My friend's <u>name is</u> Rasheed and ¹_____ fourteen years old. Rasheed is ²_____, but friendly. ³_____ football and volleyball, but he ⁴_____ shopping. He often ⁵_____ football and ⁶_____ manga comics, and he spends his money on ⁷_____.

He wants to chat with ⁸_____ 14–16, and he speaks ⁹_____. He wants to ¹⁰_____ German and how to ¹¹_____.

4 ⭐⭐⭐ Write a description of your friend. Use the text in exercise 3 to help you.

PROGRESS REVIEW ● Unit 1

MY EVALUATION **Check your progress. Do the exercises and then complete your own evaluation.**

◼◻◻◻ I need to try this again.   ◼◼◼◻ I am happy with this.

◼◼◻◻ I could do this better.   ◼◼◼◼ I can do this very well.

VOCABULARY ● Everyday objects

1 **Complete the crossword.**

Across

1 Can I use your _____ phone to make a call?
4 I use my _____ to listen to my music.
5 I haven't got any _____, so I can't go shopping.
8 Keep your money safe in a _____.
9 Don't forget your _____. You don't want to pay for a full-price bus ticket.

Down

2 I really want a _____, so I can surf the internet when I go out.
3 You need a student ID _____ to get cheap tickets to this show.
4 You aren't allowed to wear _____ on your face at school.
6 I haven't got my _____, so I can't open the door.
7 I've got two _____ for my school books – a small, old one, and a big, new one.

> **I can talk about my possessions.**
> MY EVALUATION ◻◻◻◻

READING ● People's possessions

2 **Match sentence halves 1–6 with a–f.**

1 At my school,   ___
2 In the UK, most children   ___
3 At school, I   ___
4 We aren't   ___
5 Are you   ___
6 Is wearing jewellery   ___

a allowed to have mobile phones at school.
b allowed at your school?
c we aren't supposed to wear make-up.
d allowed to wear your own clothes to school?
e are supposed to have swimming lessons at school.
f am supposed to wear a special uniform.

> **I can talk about school rules.**
> MY EVALUATION ◻◻◻◻

LANGUAGE FOCUS ● Present simple: affirmative and negative

3 **Make present simple sentences.**

1 I / not go / cycling

_____

2 my brother / study / French and German

_____

3 he / not play / the guitar

_____

4 we / not carry / our mobile phones to school

_____

5 my sister / finish / her homework before dinner

_____

6 my dog / not like / swimming

_____

> **I can talk about habits and facts.**
> MY EVALUATION ◻◻◻◻

VOCABULARY ◼ Free-time activities

4 Complete the sentences with the correct form of a suitable verb.

1 We _____ the internet at a café. It's too expensive! ✗

2 Bruno _____ swimming at the weekends. ✔

3 Mike _____ his friends after school. ✔

4 _____ (Sara) photos on her mobile phone **?**

5 I _____ my guitar. I find it boring. ✗

6 _____ (your parents) to the radio **?**

7 My sister _____ postcards. She's got 150! ✔

8 Alex _____ films at the cinema in the town centre. ✗

> **I can talk about my free time.**
>
> MY EVALUATION ☐☐☐☐

LANGUAGE FOCUS ◼ Present simple: questions

5 Choose the correct words then answer the questions.

1 **Do / Are** you study French at school?
_____

2 **Ben listens to / Does Ben listen to** the radio?
_____

3 **Do / Does** your mum surf the internet in the evening?
_____

4 Does your dad **like / likes** coffee?
_____

5 **Do / Does** your friends play tennis?
_____

6 **Do / Does** you watch a lot of DVDs?
_____

> **I can ask and answer about free-time activities.**
>
> MY EVALUATION ☐☐☐☐

SPEAKING ◼ Asking for and giving opinions

6 Complete the dialogues.

1 **Anna** Don't you _____ these trousers?
  Jack Not much.

2 **Tom** Do you like swimming?
  Amy It's _____, I suppose.

3 **Emily** I love reading.
  Josh I can't _____ it.

4 **Adam** I love this shop. _____ do you reckon?
  Sam It's not bad.

5 **Sara** Do you like this song?
  Peter No, I'm not very _____ on it.

> **I can ask for and give opinions.**
>
> MY EVALUATION ☐☐☐☐

WRITING ◼ An internet profile

7 Complete the internet profile with the words in the box.

> prefer   mind   mad   really   keen
> into   fan

+

• Lenka • 15 years old • Czech Republic

✉ Message   👪 Add to friends

About me
Hi, I'm Lenka and I'm from Prague in the Czech Republic. I've got green eyes and long, blonde hair.

Likes and dislikes
I'm ¹_____ films, especially animated ones. I'm a big ²_____ of the film directors Tim Burton and Henry Selick. I'm not ³_____ about listening to the radio, but I use my MP3 player all the time.

My free time
I'm very ⁴_____ on surfing the internet. I've got my own website and blog, and I'm ⁵_____ into it. I spend hours on the internet every day! I ⁶_____ using my laptop, because my brother always uses our desktop computer at home.

Requests
I want to meet someone of a similar age to me. I don't ⁷_____ where you're from, but I want to practise my English, please.

> **I can write about my likes and dislikes.**
>
> MY EVALUATION ☐☐☐☐

VOCABULARY ■ At home

1 ⭐ Look at the picture. Write the correct numbers.

> bookcase _1_   picture ___
> bed ___   mirror ___
> chest of drawers ___   table ___
> cupboard ___   lamp ___
> chair ___

2 ⭐⭐ Do the *Furniture quiz*. Use the words in the box.

> bath   sofa   desk   microwave   wardrobe
> ~~shower~~   washing machine

Furniture quiz: What is it?

This is in the bathroom. You wash your hair in it. Water comes down on your head.
___shower___

1 You keep your clothes in this. _____

2 You sit on this with your family and watch TV. _____

3 When your clothes are dirty, you wash them in this. _____

4 This is in the kitchen. You can cook your favourite food in it very quickly.
_____

5 This is a table. You do your homework on it. _____

6 You put a lot of water in this and then wash your body. _____

3 ⭐⭐ Complete the text with the words in the box.

> dining room   bathroom   ~~living room~~
> bedrooms   kitchen

Holiday flat

Come and stay in this beautiful flat next to the sea in Bournemouth! There's a big ___living room___ with a very comfortable sofa – you can sit on this and watch DVDs, read or relax.

There's also a wonderful [1]_____ – it's got a new microwave and a washing machine, too. Cook a meal for all your family in here!

The flat has got a nice [2]_____ with big windows. You can eat dinner and look at the beach.

There are two big [3]_____ – they're both very quiet and you can sleep well here. Next to these two rooms there's an excellent [4]_____ with a big bath and a hot shower.

Contact us for more information.

4 ⭐⭐⭐ Write sentences to describe your bedroom. What furniture is there, and where is it? Use the prepositions in the box.

> behind   between   in front of   near
> next to   on   under

There's a big wardrobe. It's next to my bed.

1 _____

2 _____

3 _____

4 _____

5 _____

6 _____

1 ⭐ Complete the table with *is*, *are* or *am*, and the *-ing* form of the verbs.

Subject	*be*	*-ing* form
Affirmative		
I	__am__	working. (work)
		sitting. (sit)
You / We / They	¹_____	_____ (play)
		_____ (do)
He / She / It	²_____	_____ (read)
		_____ (give)
Negative		_____ (stop)
		_____ (swim)
I	³_____ not	_____ (cry)
		_____ (listen)
You / We / They	⁴_____n't	_____ (change)
		_____ (make)
He / She / It	⁵_____n't	

2 ⭐⭐ What are the people doing? Complete the sentences using the present continuous form of the verbs in the box.

> study   surf   sleep   ~~have~~   wash
> read   watch

My family is in the kitchen. They **'re having** breakfast.

1 I'm at my desk. I _____ for my exam tomorrow.
2 Danny is on the sofa in the living room. He _____ TV.
3 My grandfather is in the bedroom. He _____ the newspaper.
4 Hanif and Daniel are on the computer. They _____ the internet.
5 My sister is in the bathroom. She _____ her hands and face.
6 My grandmother is in bed. She _____.

3 ⭐⭐ Write affirmative and negative sentences using the present continuous.

Adrian / not work on the computer / play a game

Adrian isn't working on the computer.

He's playing a game.

1 Anna / not read her book / look out of the window

_____

_____

2 you / not listen to the teacher / talk

_____

_____

3 I / send a text on my mobile phone / not make a call

_____

_____

4 Lena / not sit in her chair / run to the door

_____

_____

5 we / read a magazine / not do our homework

_____

_____

6 Freddie and Sara / eat some biscuits / not study

_____

_____

4 ⭐⭐⭐ Choose six of your favourite photos. Write one positive and one negative sentence about each one. What are the people doing / not doing?

In my favourite photo of my parents they're swimming in the sea. They aren't lying on the beach.

1 _____

_____

2 _____

_____

3 _____

_____

4 _____

_____

5 _____

_____

6 _____

_____

1 ⭐ Choose the correct words.

They always (take) / clear out the rubbish at the weekend.

1 My brother often **tidies** / **does** the washing-up after dinner.
2 My mum usually **cleans** / **makes** the floor in the kitchen.
3 Do you ever **take** / **do** the dog for a walk?
4 Carlos sometimes **makes** / **cleans** his bed in the morning.
5 You never **make** / **tidy** your room.
6 I always **do** / **clear** the table after dinner.

2 ⭐⭐ Complete the sentences using the correct form of the verbs in the box.

> do   clear   tidy   do   take   ~~make~~
> clean

My sister likes helping at home. She always **makes** her bed before school.

1 Can you _____ the table, please?
2 My friend Nils usually _____ out the rubbish.
3 After lunch, they always _____ the washing-up.
4 My cousin is very lazy and he never _____ his room.
5 We need to _____ the floor. It's really dirty!
6 My brother never _____ the ironing or vacuuming.

3 ⭐⭐ Complete the dialogue with the words in the box.

> ~~your bed~~   the shopping   your room
> the vacuuming   the car   the washing-up
> the ironing

Pete Can I have £5 to go out, Mum?
Mum £5? You're joking! You don't help around the house at all. You never make **your bed**, or tidy ¹_____. I can't do ²_____ in there, because there are clothes and magazines on the floor!
Pete Okay, okay, I'm going. What else do you want me to do?
Mum If you want £5, you can do ³_____ after lunch, and you can clean ⁴_____ before Dad goes to the supermarket to do ⁵_____.
Pete All that for £5? All right then. But Mum …
Mum Yes?
Pete Can you do ⁶_____? I want to wear my new shirt to go out!

4 ⭐⭐⭐ Who usually helps around the house in your family? Is anyone doing anything now? Which jobs do people like / dislike? Write sentences. Use some of the words in the box.

regular activities	sometimes, usually, never
activities now	now, at the moment
likes and dislikes	prefers, likes, hates + -ing form

<u>My sister and I sometimes help with the shopping.</u>

1 _____
   _____
2 _____
   _____
3 _____
   _____
4 _____
   _____
5 _____
   _____
6 _____
   _____

Present continuous: questions

1 ★ Complete the table with the words in the box.

> are   aren't   ~~am~~   is   'm not   is   doing

Questions			
be	Subject	*-ing* form	Other words
_Am_	I		
¹_____	you	²_____	the ironing?
³_____	she		
Short answers			
Affirmative			
Yes, I am. / Yes, you are. / Yes, she ⁴_____.			
Negative			
No, I ⁵_____. / No, you ⁶_____. / No, she isn't.			

2 ★★ Look at the picture. Write questions using the present continuous. Then write answers.

what / Ben / listen to

<u>What is Ben listening to?</u>

<u>He's listening to the radio.</u>

1 where / Kelly and Ben / sit

_____

_____

2 what / Kelly / wear

_____

_____

3 they / watch TV

_____

_____

4 Kelly / write / a text message

_____

_____

3 ★★★ Make present continuous questions about the picture in exercise 2. Then write answers.

1 Is _____?

_____

2 Who _____?

_____

3 Are _____?

_____

4 What _____?

_____

Present simple and present continuous

4 ★★ Complete the sentences using the present simple or present continuous form of the verbs.

Carlos **makes** (make) his bed every morning.

Kyle and Hannah **are clearing** (clear) the table now.

1 When _____ Katie normally _____ (tidy) her room?

2 Ana _____ (do) her homework at the moment, so she can't come out.

3 They always _____ (walk) to school at 8.00.

4 Are you _____ (have) lunch now?

5 ★★★ Write questions using the present simple or present continuous. Then write true answers.

what / you / usually do / on Saturday afternoon

<u>What do you usually do on Saturday afternoon?</u>

<u>I often go shopping or sometimes I play tennis.</u>

1 what / you / do / now

_____

_____

2 what / your mum / usually do / at the weekend

_____

_____

3 what / your best friend / do / at the moment

_____

_____

4 where / you / usually do / your homework

_____

_____

The best home in London?

This is Rory Blake's home in London. He lives on a houseboat. At the moment, the boat is staying on the River Thames, but in the summer, Rory's family have holidays on it – it's their holiday home, too!

A People think that houseboats are uncomfortable, but we've got everything – two bedrooms, a living room and a kitchen. There's even a 'garden' on the roof of the boat. I'm growing some herbs up there now, because I love cooking.

B Our houseboat *Marianne* is seventy years old and usually it's in the centre of London. It's a cool place to keep the boat – we're near some famous museums and a good library, and the view is great.

C The only problem is the weather. When it's windy, the boat goes up and down! Also we need to paint *Marianne* every year. In fact my dad and his friend are painting the houseboat now.

D When visitors come here, they walk into our living room first. They think it's great because it's really comfortable with a big TV, a sofa and modern paintings.

E The kitchen is my favourite room. My mum is making dinner there now. We're going to eat in our garden, on the roof!

1 ⭐ Read the text. Tick ✔ the correct box.

The text is about …

a ☐ living in London.
b ☐ an unusual home.
c ☐ the advantages of having a boat.

2 ⭐⭐ Read the text again. Match headings 1–4 with paragraphs A–E.

The best room on the boat   E

1 The city centre – a great place to be   _____
2 A good room to sit and relax   _____
3 Bad weather and *Marianne*   _____
4 A comfortable home with a garden   _____

3 ⭐⭐ Complete the sentences with information from the text.

Rory lives in **London**, on a houseboat.

1 Rory's home has got _____ bedrooms.
2 The boat is called _____.
3 Living on a boat isn't much fun when there's bad _____.
4 They _____ the houseboat every year.
5 There are modern paintings in the boat's _____.

4 ⭐⭐⭐ Answer the questions. Write complete sentences.

How many rooms has the houseboat got?
The houseboat has got four rooms.

1 What is Rory growing on the roof of the boat?
_____

2 How old is the houseboat?
_____

3 What are Rory's dad and his friend doing now?
_____

4 Why do visitors like the living room?
_____

5 What's Rory's mum doing now?
_____

Build your vocabulary

5 ⭐⭐ Complete the sentences with the words in the box.

> view   traditional   balcony   ~~windows~~
> holiday homes

My room has two large **windows**, so it's light.

1 The _____ outside my bedroom is dangerous. Don't stand on it!
2 Would you prefer a modern flat in the town centre, or a _____ house in the country?
3 The _____ from our roof is wonderful. You can see all of the city.
4 Many celebrities have _____ that they only visit once or twice a year.

Language point: *and, but, because*

1 ★ Choose the correct words.

They love the painting, **because** / **but** they don't like the mirror.

1 In the dining room there's a chest of drawers **and** / **but** a big cupboard.
2 We like the sofa **because** / **but** it's very comfortable.
3 The bedroom is small, **because** / **but** it's got everything we need.
4 There are two chairs **and** / **but** a table in the room.
5 I'm not watching TV **and** / **because** there aren't any good programmes today.
6 I haven't got a TV in my bedroom, **but** / **and** we've got a big TV in the living room.
7 I like the kitchen **because** / **but** it's got big windows.

2 ★★ Write sentences with *and*, *but* or *because*.

There's a nice sofa in our living room. We've got a big TV, too.

There's a nice sofa in our living room and we've got a big TV, too.

1 He's going to bed now. He's tired.

_____

2 I often tidy my room. I never do the washing-up.

_____

3 At school we study history. We learn French.

_____

4 We always get up early. School starts at 8.00.

_____

5 I really want that picture. I haven't got any money.

_____

● TASK

3 ★★ Complete the information about Miley Cyrus with the words in the box.

> microwave beds mother shower
> clothes films ~~drink~~ living

On tour with Miley Cyrus

When *Hannah Montana* star Miley Cyrus goes on tour she travels in a big, pink tour bus. You can do everything on the bus – eat, _drink_ , sleep and have a shower.

The first room you walk into is a big, modern ¹_____ room with a table and two comfortable brown sofas. Miley always travels with her family, and at the moment her ²_____ is doing some work at the table.

The next room is the bedroom, with comfortable ³_____. At night Miley can watch her favourite ⁴_____ because there's a TV next to her bed. There's also an enormous wardrobe with a lot of Miley's ⁵_____, ready for her next show.

The kitchen is quite small, but it's got everything – a fridge, a ⁶_____ and things for making coffee. There's also a cool bathroom with a ⁷_____ and a big mirror – perfect for the modern star on tour!

4 ★★★ Imagine your favourite pop star or sports star has got a tour bus. Write a description of the tour bus. Use the text in exercise 3 to help you.

MY EVALUATION   Check your progress. Do the exercises and then complete your own evaluation.

☑☐☐☐ I need to try this again.   ☑☑☑☐ I am happy with this.

☑☑☐☐ I could do this better.   ☑☑☑☑ I can do this very well.

VOCABULARY ● At home

1   Match sentence halves 1–6 with a–f.

1 I can't read my book, because   ___
2 We've got a shower in our bathroom,   ___
3 I've got a desk in my room, so   ___
4 We normally sit on the sofa   ___
5 Have you got a chest of   ___
6 We only eat in the dining room   ___

a but we haven't got a bath.
b drawers in your bedroom?
c the lamp next to my bed isn't working.
d when we have a special meal with visitors.
e to watch TV.
f I can do my homework there.

> **I can describe the position of objects.**
> MY EVALUATION   ☐☐☐☐

READING ● Seeing stars

2   Complete the description of a celebrity's home with the words in the box.

> view   traditional   balcony   windows
> holiday home

This lovely house is our celebrity's ¹_____, not his full-time residence. He comes here two or three times a year for a short break, to see friends, swim, go sailing or fishing. The ²_____ of the sea from the house is magnificent. The main bedroom has enormous ³_____, so you can look down to the house's beautiful private beach. The house is over 100 years old and is very ⁴_____. There is a large ⁵_____ outside the living room, and it is famous for the parties which they have there.

> **I can understand adverts and postcards.**
> MY EVALUATION   ☐☐☐☐

LANGUAGE FOCUS ● Present continuous: affirmative and negative

3   Complete the sentences with the present continuous affirmative (✓) or negative (✗) form of the verbs in the box.

> chat   go   make   meet   watch   finish

1 They _____ to the museum at the moment. ✓
2 We _____ a film on TV. ✗
3 He _____ to his friends on the internet. ✓
4 I _____ Sara today. ✗
5 Miley Cyrus _____ her new TV show today. ✗
6 I _____ my homework now. ✓

> **I can describe what is happening.**
> MY EVALUATION   ☐☐☐☐

VOCABULARY ● Housework

4   Complete the crossword.

		1				2				3		
								4	W	A	L	K
5			6		7							
			8									
9												
		10										

Across

4 I'm taking the dog for a _____ now.

5 I don't _____ my room very often.

7 How often do you _____ the shopping?

8 Can you take the _____ out now, please? It smells bad!

9 Please clean the _____ in the bathroom.

10 Does your sister _____ her bed every day?

Down

1 I usually make my _____ after I get up.

2 I'm doing the _____ at the moment, so you can wear your shirt tonight.

3 How often do you _____ the table after dinner?

4 Dan never does the _____-up!

5 We _____ the dog out to the park every afternoon.

6 Go and tidy _____ _____ now!

I can talk about helping at home.

MY EVALUATION ☐☐☐☐

LANGUAGE FOCUS ▪ Present simple and present continuous

5 Complete the sentences. Use the present simple or the present continuous form of the verbs.

do   not wear   arrive   talk   not go   have

1 She _____ her homework at the moment.

2 I _____ to school on Sundays.

3 What time _____ they _____ dinner on Mondays?

4 It's very hot. We _____ jackets today.

5 They always _____ home at six o'clock.

6 You're on the phone again! _____ you _____ to David?

I can contrast present actions with routines.

MY EVALUATION ☐☐☐☐

SPEAKING ▪ Making requests and compromises

6 Choose the correct words.

Dad Hello, Millie.

Millie Hi, Dad.

Dad Can you ¹**tidy / make** the living room, please? All your things are ²**on / up** the sofa.

Millie Yes, ³**in / at** a minute. I'm busy at the ⁴**hour / moment**.

Dad Come ⁵**off / on**, Millie. It's important!

Millie But I'm ⁶**doing / having** my homework now.

Dad Millie! You ⁷**need / make** to tidy the living room now!

Millie Please, Dad! Is it ⁸**right / OK** if I do it later?

Dad I ⁹**suppose / want** so, but don't forget to ¹⁰**make / do** it before you go to bed.

Millie OK, Dad!

I can make requests and compromises.

MY EVALUATION ☐☐☐☐

WRITING ▪ A perfect place to live

7 Complete the sentences with *and*, *but* or *because*.

1 There are photos on the wall, _____ no paintings _____ my dad is a keen photographer.

2 Our sofa is quite small _____ it's old, _____ it's very comfortable.

3 I love these windows _____ there is a great view of the sea, _____ I spend a lot of time looking out of them.

4 Our living room is modern _____ it's got a fantastic new TV, _____ I think it's a boring room.

5 I like my room _____ it's my favourite colour, _____ I want a bigger one.

I can describe my ideal home.

MY EVALUATION ☐☐☐☐

VOCABULARY ● Adjectives: feelings and events

1 ★ Find six more adjectives.

F	A	N	E	Y	A	X	C	I	L
S	Q	A	B	P	W	D	U	K	U
S	C	U	O	H	G	G	T	T	C
Z	U	G	G	U	F	E	E	V	K
A	N	H	O	P	P	K	L	J	Y
R	E	T	O	S	Y	N	K	X	O
Y	Q	Y	N	E	R	V	O	U	S
A	R	E	V	T	H	I	U	A	Y
F	C	R	D	L	O	N	E	L	Y
Z	P	B	S	C	A	R	Y	L	Z

cute

_____   _____

_____   _____

_____   _____

2 ★★ Complete the adjectives in the sentences.

My sister is n**aughty**. She doesn't listen to Mum.

1 Megan is u_____ because James isn't talking to her.
2 The baby was sleeping. She was very c_____.
3 I'm sometimes l_____ at weekends when I don't meet my friends.
4 Clara often wins prizes. She's very l_____.
5 Jamie's n_____ because he's got an exam tomorrow.
6 I can't sleep after horror films, because I find them very s_____!

3 ★★ Look at the picture and complete the text with the words in the box.

> cute   lonely   lucky   naughty   nervous   scary   ~~upset~~

This is a photo of my sister Lucy's sixth birthday party. She's the girl crying. She was _upset_ because her friend, Harry, pulled her hair. He was always very ¹_____.

Also, Lucy was frightened of the clown – she thought he was ²_____.

Our cousin, Daniel, is at the back. He was feeling ³_____ because nobody played with him. He was ⁴_____ too because he doesn't like meeting new people.

That's me in the front. I look really ⁵_____ in that dress! I was the ⁶_____ one that day – I had a great time.

4 ★★★ Think about important events from your childhood. Who was: nervous / upset / lucky / naughty / lonely? What was: scary / cute? Write sentences.

<u>I was very nervous on my 8th birthday.</u>

<u>My first day at school was quite scary.</u>

1 _____
2 _____
3 _____
4 _____
5 _____

1 ⭐ Complete the tables with *was*, *were*, *wasn't* or *weren't*.

	Subject	was(n't) / were(n't)	Other words
Affirmative	I / He / She You / We / They	_was_ [1]_____	at the party.
Negative	I / He / She You / We / They	[2]_____ [3]_____	naughty. very angry. at home.

Questions			Answers
(Question word)	was / were	Subject + other words	(Yes / No) + subject + was(n't) / were(n't)
	[4]_____	Jamie late?	Yes, he [5]_____. No, he [6]_____.
	[7]_____	they happy?	Yes, they [8]_____. No, they [9]_____.
Who	[10]_____	upset last night?	Frances was upset.
What	[11]_____	their names?	Their names were Dan and Sal.

2 ⭐ Choose the correct words.

I (was) / were tired last night.

1 The men **was** / **were** angry.
2 The party **wasn't** / **didn't was** fun.
3 **Was the film** / **The film was** interesting? No, it **not** / **wasn't**.
4 Where **were you** / **you were** born?
5 **Were** / **was** the girls nervous? No, they **weren't** / **wasn't**.
6 Who **was your favourite teacher** / **your favourite teacher was**?

3 ⭐⭐ Write sentences in the past.

Honza is my best friend.
<u>Honza was my best friend.</u>

1 That film is really scary!
_____

2 My baby brothers are naughty at bedtime.
_____

3 Is Tina at school today? No, she isn't.
_____

4 I'm not happy about moving house.
_____

5 Who is the owner of that bike?
_____

6 Are Mel and Ivana friends? Yes, they are.
_____

4 ⭐⭐ Order the words to make sentences and questions with *was* and *were*.

the / at / was / party / Jamie / ?
<u>Was Jamie at the party?</u>

1 were / my / doctors / grandparents
_____

2 at / yesterday / Mikhail / school / wasn't
_____

3 May / fourteen / 1st / Katja / on / was
_____

4 late / you / were / school / for / ?
_____

5 good / tennis / they / very / at / weren't
_____

6 your / school / a student / at this / sister / was / ?
_____

5 ⭐⭐⭐ Your friend lost her bag and shoes yesterday. Look at the information about them. Use the prompts to make questions and short answers.

bag	shoes
big red new	green old size 40

bag / green
<u>Was the bag green?</u>
<u>No, it wasn't.</u>

shoes / size 40
<u>Were the shoes size 40?</u>
<u>Yes, they were.</u>

1 bag / new
_____
_____?

2 bag / old
_____?

3 shoes / red
_____?

4 bag / small
_____?

5 shoes / green
_____?

6 shoes / new
_____?

1 ✯ Look at the pictures and choose the correct verbs. Then write the past simple form.

(get)/ have married
_____got_____

1 grow / go to school
_____

2 move / do an exam
_____

3 leave / win a competition
_____

4 have / leave home
_____

5 buy / be a house
_____

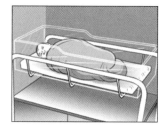

6 be / get born
_____

7 leave / become school
_____

2 ✯✯ Complete the sentences using the past simple form of the words in the box.

go be leave become get move

Angelina Jolie _____was_____ born on 4th June 1975.

1 Her family _____ to Los Angeles when Jolie was 11.

2 She _____ to an acting school for three years.

3 When she was 16, she _____ home for the first time.

4 She _____ really famous with the film *Girl, Interrupted* in 1999.

5 She _____ married to two different men before she met Brad Pitt.

3 ✯✯ Look at the table. What did Jack do? Write affirmative sentences.

graduate ✓	buy a house ✓
leave home ✓	get married ✓
get a job ✓	have a child ✓

He graduated.

1 _____

2 _____

3 _____

4 _____

5 _____

4 ✯✯✯ Write six sentences about the life of your grandparents, or an old person you know. Use verbs from exercises 1–3 and the expressions in the box.

in 1967 / 1984   when he / she was ...
at the age of ...   from ... to ...   for ... years

My grandmother was born in 1948. From 1953-1962, she went to school. At the age of 14, she ...

1 _____

2 _____

3 _____

4 _____

5 _____

6 _____

LANGUAGE FOCUS ■ Past simple • Time expressions and *ago*

Past simple

1 ★ Complete the tables with the words in the box.

> did left ~~started~~ like start didn't
> did when

	Subject	Past form	Other words
Affirmative	I / You / He / She / We / They	<u>started</u> liked ¹_____	school.
Negative	I / You / He / She / We / They	²_____	start ³_____ leave school.

(Question word)	*did*	Subject	Verb	Other words	Answers
	Did	you	like	school?	Yes, I ⁴_____. No, I didn't.
⁵_____	⁶_____	he	⁷_____	school?	He started school in 2005.

2 ★★ Write affirmative and negative past simple sentences and questions.

he / become / a professional

<u>He became a professional.</u>

<u>He didn't become a professional.</u>

<u>Did he become a professional?</u>

1 you / win / a computer

_____
_____
_____

2 they / buy / a house

_____
_____
_____

3 Sheena / do / the exam

_____
_____
_____

4 Rob and Alice / get married

_____
_____
_____

3 ★★★ Write questions about Florence Nightingale, a famous nurse from 19th-century England. Then write answers for the questions. Use the information.

1 not go to school   4 go to help soldiers
2 become a nurse   5 not get married
3 go to Turkey   6 die 1910

be born 1820
When <u>was she born? She was born in 1820.</u>
1 Did _____.
2 What _____.
3 Where _____.
4 Why _____.
5 Did _____.
6 When _____.

Time expressions and *ago*

4 ★★ Write sentences using the past simple and *ago* in the correct place.

a year / I start / a new school

<u>A year ago I started a new school.</u>

1 we / move / to a big house / three years

_____

2 two days / my mum / get / a new job

_____

3 six weeks / Lily / buy / a mobile phone

_____

4 my brother / leave school / two years

_____

5 half an hour / I / have lunch

_____

6 we / go to the USA / six months

_____

1 ⭐ Read the text. Tick ✔ the correct box.

The text is about …

a ☐ memory competitions.
b ☐ where animals put their food.
c ☐ human and animal memories.

The best memory

Who's got the best memory: humans or animals? It's an interesting question.

Several years ago, a group of scientists tested the photographic memory of young chimpanzees. They showed chimpanzees and humans a computer screen with numbers on it. When the numbers disappeared, the chimpanzees could remember the position of the numbers. In fact they were better at this than the humans.

Their experiments showed that a bird called Clark's nutcracker had a fantastic memory, too. The scientists watched the birds for months. The birds hid thousands of seeds over an area of about twenty square kilometres. Six months later the birds found nearly all of the seeds from memory. Humans were far less successful at this type of activity.

However, humans can do something that animals can't do. We can decide how we want to memorize things. In the scientists' memory experiments, humans used different techniques to memorize objects. Some imagined pictures of the objects, and some said the words to themselves again and again. Humans wrote lists and trained their brains not to forget important information. Animals can't do that!

2 ⭐⭐ Read the text again. Complete the sentences.

Scientists tested chimpanzees and humans.

1 The _____ did better in the number tests.
2 Clark's nutcrackers have got very good _____.
3 Clark's nutcrackers _____ their seeds.
4 The birds _____ nearly all of the seeds.
5 We write lists so we don't _____ things.

3 ⭐⭐⭐ Answer the questions. Write complete sentences.

What ability did the scientists test?

They tested memory.

1 What could the chimpanzees remember?
_____

2 How many seeds did the birds hide?
_____

3 How big was the area that the birds used?
_____

4 When did the birds return to look for the seeds?
_____

5 What can humans do that animals can't?
_____

Build your vocabulary

4 ⭐⭐ Complete the sentences with the words in the box.

> memorize   memory   photographic
> ~~from memory~~   recited   remember

I can tell you my friends' birthdays _from memory_.

1 My grandma is 85, but she still has a fantastic _____.
2 Did you _____ to bring my CD? Great, thanks.
3 The teacher gave us some vocabulary to _____ for homework.
4 I've got a _____ memory. I can read a list of words and remember them all!
5 Yesterday Jen _____ a really long poem in class.

Language point: *there was, there were*

1 ★ Read the email and choose the correct words.

```
●●●
⊘      ◄      ◄◄      ►      ✎      📁      ✉      Q- From
Delete  Reply  Reply All  Forward  New  Mailboxes  Get Mail              Search Mailb
```

Hi Ollie!

We had a brilliant weekend in London. I went there with Mum and Tina on the train. There **was** / **were** great museums, and ¹**was** / **there** was a lot to see. ²**It** / **There** was great!

First, we went to the Natural History Museum. There ³**was** / **were** a giant dinosaur near the entrance. ⁴**Were there** / **There were** lots of small children too, and ⁵**they** / **there** were really noisy! After that, we went shopping in Kensington Market. There ⁶**was** / **were** some fantastic clothes. I got a new pair of jeans.

How was your weekend?

Love
Lottie x

---

2 ★★ Match questions 1–6 with answers a–f.

1 How many people were there? ___f___
2 How was the museum? _____
3 Was there any music? _____
4 Were there many people? _____
5 Were your friends at the party? _____
6 Was there any food? _____

a It was really interesting.
b No, there wasn't. Tim ate it before we arrived!
c No, they weren't. It was really boring!
d Yes, there was. My brother was the DJ.
e No, there weren't.
f There were about twelve, I think.

○ TASK

3 ★★ Complete the email using the past simple form of the verbs in the box.

> have   get up   be   fly   eat   play   ~~visit~~   be   enjoy   be   go

```
●●●
⊘      ◄      ◄◄      ►      ✎      📁      ✉      Q- From
Delete  Reply  Reply All  Forward  New  Mailboxes  Get Mail        Search Mailbox
```

Hi Michelle,

I ___visited___ my cousins in Monte Carlo last weekend. First, there ¹_____ a party at their flat on Friday night. There ²_____ lots of interesting people there. Then, we ³_____ quite late on Saturday. We ⁴_____ breakfast in a street café. After that, we ⁵_____ volleyball on the beach. Later, we ⁶_____ out to a nightclub. Finally, I ⁷_____ back home on Sunday afternoon.

I ⁸_____ a great time! I ⁹_____ seeing my cousins – it ¹⁰_____ a lot of fun.

Love, Laura

4 ★★★ Write an email to a friend about a good weekend. Use the words in the box or your own ideas. Don't forget to include time linkers in your email.

play	football / computer games / tennis
go	shopping / camping / to the cinema / to the beach
buy	new jeans / DVDs / a mobile phone
see	a film / a football match / a show

MY EVALUATION   Check your progress. Do the exercises and then complete your own evaluation.

◉◯◯◯ I need to try this again.   ◉◉◉◯ I am happy with this.
◉◉◯◯ I could do this better.   ◉◉◉◉ I can do this very well.

VOCABULARY ● Adjectives: feelings and events

1   Write the adjectives to describe the people or situations.

1 a horror film   s_____
2 a child that doesn't do what his parents say n_____
3 a student before an exam   n_____
4 the winner of a £1 million prize l_____
5 someone with no friends   l_____
6 a baby animal sleeping   c_____
7 a small child with broken toys u_____

I can describe feelings and events.

MY EVALUATION   ◻◻◻◻

READING ● Remember this!

2   Choose the correct words to complete the sentences.

1 I can say all of my friends' mobile phone numbers **from / on** memory.
2 Mira tries to **memory / memorize** new English words every day.
3 I've got a terrible **memory / memorize** – I forget everything!
4 My **photographic / picture** memory is excellent. I have a picture in my head of where I saw things.
5 We **photographed / recited** our irregular verbs in English. We remembered them all!
6 Can you **memorize / remember** the house you grew up in?

I can understand a text about people with good memories.

MY EVALUATION   ◻◻◻◻

LANGUAGE FOCUS ● was, were

3   Complete the text with the correct form of was or were.

It [1]_____ the night of my fourteenth birthday party. There [2]_____ nice things to eat, and the music at the party [3]_____ great. But my friends [4]_____ there. Where [5]_____ they? I [6]_____ happy. [7]_____ there a problem? Then I heard a noise outside. What [8]_____ it? I looked out of the window. My friends [9]_____ in the garden! Soon there [10]_____ a lot of people at the party. It [11]_____ a great evening!

I can talk about past events in my life.

MY EVALUATION   ◻◻◻◻

VOCABULARY ● Milestones

4   Complete the text with the words in the box.

left   become   up   get   married   job
had   born   became

Johnny Depp was [1]_____ in Kentucky, but he grew [2]_____ in Florida. He [3]_____ school when he was only 15, because he wanted to [4]_____ a rock star. He got [5]_____ when he was 20 years old, but got divorced two years later. He got his first acting [6]_____ with the help of actor Nick Cage, and he [7]_____ rich and famous after working on *Edward Scissorhands* and the *Pirates of the Caribbean* films. He met his partner Vanessa Paradis in France. They [8]_____ children together in 1999 and 2002, but they didn't [9]_____ married.

I can talk about important life events.

MY EVALUATION   ◻◻◻◻

LANGUAGE FOCUS ■ Past simple

5 Complete the sentences using the past simple form of the verbs in the box.

> have   ~~graduate~~   not be born   leave
> buy   do   get   start

1 When **did she graduate** from university?
2 She _____ school in 1980 and left in 1992.
3 _____ Jake _____ home two years ago?
4 My uncle _____ a house in London.
5 _____ he _____ the exam?
6 They _____ a baby last year.
7 You _____ in 1993.
8 My parents met in 1987 and they _____ married two years later.

> **I can talk about past events.**
>
> MY EVALUATION ☐☐☐☐

SPEAKING ■ Your weekend

6 Match questions 1–6 with answers a–f.

1 How was your weekend? ___
2 When did you last play basketball? ___
3 Where did you go at the weekend? ___
4 I went to my friend's house last night. What about you? ___
5 Who's that girl in the photo? ___
6 When did you go home? ___

a When the shops closed – about 6 p.m.
b We went to London.
c Oh, I watched a film at home.
d I don't know, maybe three weeks ago.
e It looks like Alicia.
f Not bad, thanks.

> **I can talk about experiences in the past.**
>
> MY EVALUATION ☐☐☐☐

WRITING ■ A past event

7 Order the words to make sentences. Then number the sentences 1–5 to make a story.

a ☐ into / lunch / I / then / meet / for / town / to / went / him

_____

_____

b ☐ came / we / very / finally / late / home

_____

_____

c ☐ the / film / after / saw / at / we / a / cinema / that

_____

_____

d ☐ phone / Marco / call / I / from / first / my / got / friend / a

_____

_____

e ☐ day / had / lovely / Saturday / last / I / a

_____

> **I can describe an event in the past.**
>
> MY EVALUATION ☐☐☐☐

VOCABULARY ■ Prepositions: movement

1 ★ Match sentence halves 1–6 with a–f.

1 Chris Bromham jumped   _c_
2 Chad Hundeby swam   ___
3 Iris Alvarez jumped   ___
4 Michael Johnson ran   ___
5 Takao Arayama climbed   ___
6 Joseph Kittinger fell   ___

a through the air for 31,000 metres in the world's highest skydive.
b up Mount Everest when he was 70 years old.
c over 18 big red buses on his motorbike.
d into the sea from an 18-metre rock.
e across the sea from England to France in 7 hours and 17 minutes.
f around a 400-metre track in 43.18 seconds.

2 ★★ Choose the correct answers.

I always cycle slowly so I don't fall _____ my bike.

  a up b down c (off) d around
1 At the moment they're driving _____ Europe.
  a across b up c down d off
2 She's very good at winter sports. She can ski _____ that mountain in three minutes.
  a through b down c out of d under
3 Tom climbed _____ the tree to get an apple.
  a off b under c around d up
4 Last year Maria jumped _____ a plane at 1,000 metres.
  a out of b around c up d through
5 In July we cycled _____ the mountains in Italy.
  a off b through c under d out of

3 ★★ Complete the sentences with the words in the box.

> climb down   run into   ~~cycle through~~
> sail around   fall off   run around
> swim across

For their next holiday they want to __cycle through__ the north of Germany.

1 After the goal the footballers began to _____ the stadium.
2 Be careful! Don't _____ that chair and break your leg.
3 It's very hot today! Let's _____ the sea and cool down!
4 It's impossible to _____ the Atlantic!
5 If you really love the sea, why don't you _____ the world?
6 We need to _____ the mountain now because it's getting dark.

4 ★★★ Write sentences about what you want to do when you're older. Use the words in the boxes and your own ideas.

> drive across   ski down   climb up
> cycle across   jump out of   walk under

> Africa   the United States   Australia
> the Mediterranean   Mount Etna
> a plane   Mount Fuji   the Sahara Desert
> a big waterfall

<u>When I'm older, I want to drive across the</u>
<u>United States.</u>

1 _____
2 _____
3 _____
4 _____
5 _____
6 _____

1 Complete the table with the words in the box.

> wasn't   ~~was~~   were   weren't

	Subject	was(n't) / were(n't)	-ing form
Affirmative	I / He / She / It	<u>was</u>	sleeping. studying. travelling. dancing. working.
	You / We / They	¹_____	
Negative	I / He / She / It	²_____	
	You / We / They	³_____	

2 ★ Complete the sentences with *was*, *were*, *wasn't* or *weren't*.

We ___<u>were</u>___ having dinner at eight o'clock last night. We had chicken and chips.

1 In this photo we _____ visiting Mexico City.

2 Mohammed _____ reading a magazine in class. He was studying.

3 Look at this holiday video of my sister. She _____ swimming in a lake.

4 You weren't listening to the teacher. You _____ looking at your mobile phone.

5 I _____ wearing a sweater yesterday because it was very hot.

6 They _____ cycling through Poland in June. They were driving.

3 ★★ Write affirmative or negative sentences using the past continuous.

I / walk / across the park / yesterday
<u>I was walking across the park yesterday.</u>

1 Gina / play / football / an hour ago
_____

2 they / climb down / the mountain / at seven o'clock yesterday evening
_____

3 she / not ski / this time last Saturday
_____

4 Naomi and Paul / swim / half an hour ago
_____

5 it / not rain / this afternoon
_____

6 you / sail / at this time last Sunday
_____

4 ★★ Complete the text using the past continuous form of the verbs in the box.

> not listen   have   sail   ~~not study~~
> watch   relax   cycle   not do

Last week my friends and I <u>weren't studying</u> at school and we ¹_____ to our teacher. We ²_____ fun on an adventure holiday! Ian and Tom ³_____ down a mountain on their bikes, and I ⁴_____ across a lake. But my twin sister Nadia ⁵_____ exciting things. She ⁶_____ in her room at the hotel with her friends and they ⁷_____ TV!

5 ★★★ Write about your last birthday. Write one affirmative and one negative sentence for each time.

> 7.30 a.m.   11.00 a.m.   1.00 p.m.   4.00 p.m.
> 8.00 p.m.   midnight

<u>At 7.30 a.m. I wasn't sleeping. I was opening a</u>
<u>birthday card from my parents.</u>
_____
_____
_____
_____
_____
_____
_____
_____
_____
_____
_____

1 ★ Label the photos.

sea

1 _____

2 _____   3 _____

4 _____   5 _____

6 _____   7 _____

2 ★★ Read the definitions. Complete the words.

This is a big place with a lot of trees.

___forest___

1 This is a lot of water in one place.
  s_____
2 This is a place at the top and bottom of the world. p_____
3 These are very high hills. m_____
4 This is a long line of water that goes down to the sea. r_____
5 This is a very dry place with a lot of sand and rocks. d_____
6 This is where water comes down from a very high place. f_____
7 This is a very big sea. o_____

3 ★★ Do the *Geography quiz*. Choose the correct answers to complete the sentences.

Geography quiz

Lake Victoria is the largest lake in _____

a (Africa)   b North America
c Europe   d Asia

1 Between India and Nepal there are some very high mountains. They are called the _____.
  a Tatras b Pyrenees c Himalayas
  d Urals
2 The North Pole is at the top of the world. It's in _____.
  a the Arctic b the Antarctic c Asia
  d Australia
3 The longest river in the world is the _____.
  a Thames b Mississippi c Zambezi
  d Nile
4 The world's biggest hot desert is very dry. It's called the _____.
  a Sahara b Kalahari c Gobi d Atacama
5 At the highest falls in the world the water comes down 979 metres. This place is in _____.
  a France b Egypt c Australia
  d Venezuela.
6 The North Atlantic Ocean is between _____.
  a Australia and Asia
  b Europe and Antarctica
  c Europe and America   d Africa and India

4 ★★★ Write about places that you or your family visited or saw on TV. Use the words in exercises 1–3 and past time expressions.

In 2010, my grandparents went to the Balkan
mountains.
A week ago, I saw a TV programme about the
Sahara Desert.

1 _____
2 _____
3 _____
4 _____
5 _____
6 _____

Past continuous: questions

1 ★ Complete the table with the words in the box.

was were what ~~was~~ weren't were was

Questions				Answers
(Question word)	*was / were*	Subject	*-ing* form	
	Was	Lara	sleeping?	Yes, she ¹_____. / No, she wasn't.
	² _____	Mum and Dad	talking?	Yes, they were. / No, they ³_____.
⁴_____	was	Harry	reading?	He ⁵_____ reading a comic.
Where	were	you	going?	We ⁶_____ going to school.

2 ★★ Write past continuous questions.

where / Jan / go / last night

Where was Jan going last night?

1 they / have / lunch / two o'clock

_____

2 who / Mia / talk to

_____

3 what / we / do / in class last week

_____

4 it / rain / yesterday afternoon

_____

5 why / you / climb up / that big rock

_____

6 Sammi / eat / dinner / 8 p.m.

_____

3 ★★★ Mike is at a police station. There was a murder last night, and the police think Mike did it. Write three past continuous *yes / no* questions and three question-word questions for the police to ask him. Write answers for Mike.

What were you doing at 10 p.m.?

I was having dinner with my girlfriend.

1 _____

_____

2 _____

_____

3 _____

_____

4 _____

_____

5 _____

_____

6 _____

_____

Past simple and past continuous

4 ★★ Complete the sentences using the past simple or past continuous form of the verbs.

I _was climbing_ (climb) up the mountain when I ____found____ (find) a camera.

1 They _____ (swim) across the river when the boat _____ (arrive).

2 Marta _____ (have) a bad accident when she _____ (ski) down a mountain in the Urals.

3 _____ Ian _____ (listen) when the teacher _____ (ask) him a question?

4 We _____ (stop) at the Great Wall when we _____ (travel) through China.

5 You _____ (not look) at the road when you _____ (fall off) your mountain bike.

6 _____ you _____ (drive) when the storm _____ (start) ?

5 ★★★ Write sentences about a holiday you had, or invent one. Use the past simple and the past continuous.

While we were cycling through New Orleans,

we saw the carnival.

1 _____

2 _____

3 _____

4 _____

5 _____

6 _____

1 ★ Read the text and choose the correct answers.

1 Where did Ewan and Charley begin their trip?
  a South Africa b France c Libya d Scotland
2 Where did they finish?
  a South Africa b Italy c Kenya d Scotland

An incredible trip

A A few years ago *Star Wars* actor Ewan McGregor and his daredevil friend, Charley Boorman, began an incredible trip from the UK to South Africa by motorbike. They started in Scotland in May and drove through 18 countries to arrive in Cape Town in August. They made a TV programme called *Long Way Down* with their cameraman, Claudio.

B First Ewan and Charley drove down through the UK and into France. Then they went across France and through the mountains into Italy. From there, they sailed across the sea to Africa and their adventures really began!

C In Libya, they were driving across the desert when a terrible sandstorm started. And in Kenya they carried their motorbikes over a big river.

D But the most dangerous situation was in South Africa. Charley was performing stunts on his motorbike to some spectators when he hit Claudio, the cameraman. Claudio was filming when the accident happened, and he fell off his motorbike into the road. At first he didn't move, but then he stood up. The accident really hurt Claudio, but he was very brave, and continued working.

E When Ewan and Charley arrived in Cape Town, thousands of spectators and tourists were cheering for them. It was an incredible trip, but they arrived safely.

2 ★★ Read the text again. Match headings 1–4 with paragraphs A–E.

A dangerous incident	D
1 A happy end	___
2 Driving and sailing	___
3 Two continents by motorbike	___
4 Adventures in Africa	___

3 ★★★ Answer the questions. Write complete sentences.

When did Ewan and Charley start their trip?
They started their trip in May.

1 How many countries does the text mention?
_____

2 When did they finish their trip?
_____

3 Where did they go after France?
_____

4 Where were Ewan and Charley driving when they saw the sandstorm?
_____

5 What was Claudio doing when he fell off his motorbike?
_____

6 Who was waiting for them in Cape Town?
_____

4 ★★ Complete the sentences with information from the text. Use one or two words.

1 They used _____ to make their trip.
2 They spent four _____ making the trip.
3 They came through _____ between France and Italy.
4 They carried their bikes over a river in _____.
5 In South Africa, Claudio had _____.

Build your vocabulary

5 ★★ Complete the sentences with the words in the box.

> daredevils daring spectacular
> ~~stunts~~ heroes

You need a special bike to do ___*stunts*___.

1 My friends Alicia and Tom are real _____. They jumped out of a plane last year!
2 Gulay is frightened of heights, so it was very _____ of her to climb that mountain.
3 Lots of people love daredevils, but I think the real _____ are doctors.
4 The view from the top of the falls was _____.

Language point: *when, while, as soon as*

1 ★ Choose the correct words.

He saw a big fish **when** / **while** he was swimming across the lake.

1 My dad was waiting for me at the station **when** / **while** I arrived.
2 I kissed my grandmother **as soon as** / **while** she opened the door.
3 We were standing at the bus stop **when** / **while** it started to rain.
4 Elena fell over **as soon as** / **while** she was playing tennis.
5 There's a terrible car accident! Phone the police **as soon as** / **when** you can!
6 **While** / **As soon as** we were exploring the mountain, we saw a bear!

2 ★★ Match sentence halves 1–6 with a–f. Choose the correct word in brackets to join the sentences.

1 I was running to school ...   _d_
2 We opened the letter ...   ____
3 We took some photos of tigers...   ____
4 They were playing tennis ...   ____
5 I saw an amazing rescue ...   ____
6 She phoned the police ...   ____

a she saw the boy fall through the ice. (while / as soon as)
b they lost the ball. (when / while)
c we were travelling through India. (while / as soon as)
d I met my best friend. (when) / while)
e it arrived. (while / as soon as)
f I was watching the news on TV. (while / as soon as)

○ TASK

3 ★★ Read these notes for a postcard. Number the paragraphs in the correct order.

☐ Yesterday morning I was sailing in a small boat with my friend Jodie, when suddenly she stood up. I fell into the sea and it was very cold!

☐ See you soon, Isabel

1 Hi, Rosie! How are you?

☐ Then I ran up the beach to our hotel and I put on some dry clothes. I felt much better after that, but I was upset about the camera.

☐ I'm on the Isle of Wight with my class for the weekend. We're learning to sail with an instructor called Danny.

☐ As soon as Danny saw me, he came to rescue me. I was lucky because he was very near the boat when the accident happened. But while he was helping me, I dropped my camera into the water and I lost all my photos!

4 ★★★ Use the notes to write a postcard. Use the text in exercise 3 to help you.

Postcard to: Jake from Ben

Trip to: the French Alps with class for one week

Learning to: ski

Instructor: Sylvie

Problem 1: yesterday / ski down mountain / fall over

Rescue: as soon as / Sylvie / see me / ski across to me

Problem 2: while / help me / fall over again / break new sunglasses

After: go to café / feel better / be upset about sunglasses

MY EVALUATION   Check your progress. Do the exercises and then complete your own evaluation.

⬛⬜⬜⬜ I need to try this again.   ⬛⬛⬛⬜ I am happy with this.

⬛⬛⬜⬜ I could do this better.   ⬛⬛⬛⬛ I can do this very well.

VOCABULARY ● Prepositions: movement

1 Complete the dialogue with the words in the box.

> through   let's   across   down   idea   off
> don't   looks   around   climb

Jan Hey Kris, look at this 'Daredevil Adventures' holiday brochure!

Kris Daredevil Adventures? That sounds fun. What activities have they got?

Jan Well, you have lots of choices. You can ¹_____ up mountains, then ski ²_____ them again.

Kris Skiing is too expensive. ³_____ see the brochure. Ooh, this ⁴_____ fantastic. You can go camping and cycle ⁵_____ the forest.

Jan Hmm, I'm not so good at cycling. I always fall ⁶_____ my bike!

Kris OK, no cycling. Why ⁷_____ we try their 'Water Week' instead? You can sail ⁸_____ these beautiful Greek islands, and swim ⁹_____ a lake, too.

Jan That's a great ¹⁰_____. Shall we book it now? It's cheaper than the skiing week.

Kris Yes, why not?

> **I can make and respond to suggestions.**
> MY EVALUATION   ⬜⬜⬜⬜

READING ● Daredevils

2 Replace the underlined words with the words in the box.

> daring   daredevils   stunt   spectacular
> heroes

1 In this amazing and difficult physical performance, the motorcyclist jumps over 15 cars. _____

2 The stunt was amazing to watch. _____

3 Only people who love doing frightening things would try to jump off this high cliff into the sea. _____

4 The people I admire in my life are my parents. _____

5 To ski down some of the highest mountains, you have to be very ready to do things which you are frightened of. _____

> **I can read about the history of a famous place.**
> MY EVALUATION   ⬜⬜⬜⬜

LANGUAGE FOCUS ● Past continuous: affirmative and negative

3 Complete the sentences using the past continuous.

1 I _____ (not eat) breakfast at 8.00 this morning. I _____ (walk) to school.

2 We _____ (not climb) up a mountain on Friday. We _____ (relax) on the beach.

3 Lenka _____ (swim) across the lake at 6 a.m. She _____ (not sleep).

4 You _____ (not listen) to me. You _____ (look) out of the window.

5 They _____ (read) magazines. They _____ (not tidy) their bedroom.

6 I _____ (not play) football last Saturday. I _____ (visit) my cousins in London.

> **I can describe what was happening at a past event.**
> MY EVALUATION   ⬜⬜⬜⬜

VOCABULARY ● Geographical features

4 Complete the geographical features.

> I live in Cumbria, a really beautiful part of northern England. The landscape is wild and there are lots of hills and ¹m_____ that you can climb. Locally, we call them 'fells'. Between them, there are deep ²v_____. After millions of years, these filled with water, and ³l_____ were formed. The area is famous for these, and it's very popular with tourists. They like walking through the trees in the ⁴f_____ and climbing up the fells. We also have many ⁵r_____, and some of these have lovely ⁶f_____ where the water drops down the hillside. Cumbria is near the North ⁷S_____, and there are some popular beaches.

> **I can talk about places in the world.**
> MY EVALUATION ☐☐☐☐

LANGUAGE FOCUS ● Past continuous: questions

5 Make past continuous questions and answers.

1 what / you / do / last night at 11 / ?
I / sleep
_____
_____

2 Andrew and Mark / play / tennis / last night / ?
No, ...
_____
_____

3 where / you / work / last summer / ?
I / help / at my parents' shop
_____
_____

4 Hugo / win / the race before the accident / ?
Yes, ...
_____
_____

Past simple and past continuous

6 Choose the correct words.

1 He **cycled / was cycling** down the mountain when he **fell / was falling** off his bike.

2 They **drove / were driving** through Germany when they **had / were having** an accident.

3 Mikel **broke / was breaking** his leg when we **skied / were skiing** in Austria.

4 We **travelled / were travelling** on a train when he **heard / was hearing** the news.

> **I can invent a story about a world trip.**
> MY EVALUATION ☐☐☐☐

SPEAKING ● Expressing interest

7 Choose the correct words.

Clara Where did you take these photos?
Harry In Rome. This man was cycling on a tightrope.
Clara You're ¹**laughing / kidding**! Why was he doing that?
Harry There was a show in the street.
Clara ²**Right / Really**? It looks dangerous.
Harry Yes, it was ³**amazing / amazed**.
Clara It's a great photo. ⁴**Good / Well** done!
Harry And here's a nice picture of Andy. I got an extra copy for you.
Clara Wow, that's really ⁵**exciting / kind** of you. Thanks, Harry.

> **I can talk about amazing experiences.**
> MY EVALUATION ☐☐☐☐

WRITING ● A narrative text

8 Match 1–4 with a–d. Then number them in order to describe a rescue.

1 ☐ As soon as the accident happened, ___
2 ☐ Ferdi wants to go skiing again, as soon as ___
3 ☐ When they arrived to help us ___
4 ☐ We were having an adventure holiday when ___

a my brother Ferdi fell and broke his leg.
b I called the mountain rescue service.
c his leg is better! He's a real daredevil.
d we were cold and Ferdi was in a lot of pain.

> **I can write about a rescue.**
> MY EVALUATION ☐☐☐☐

5 Clever

VOCABULARY ■ Skills and people

1 ★ Write the nouns for these verbs.

paint   _painter_

1 compose   _____
2 write   _____
3 play   _____
4 dance   _____
5 win   _____
6 program   _____
7 sing   _____
8 cook   _____

2 ★★ Complete the sentences with the correct form of words in exercise 1.

Cristiano Ronaldo **plays** football.

1 Leona Lewis _____ pop songs.
2 Agatha Christie was a crime _____.
3 Mikhail Baryshnikov is a ballet _____ from Russia.
4 Bach was a _____.
5 Michelangelo was a _____.

3 ★★ Order the words to make sentences. There is one extra word in each sentence.

songs in English and Spanish / ~~wins~~ / Shakira / sings

Shakira sings songs in English and Spanish.

1 Serena Williams / a lot of / tennis matches / writes / wins

_____

2 programs / Bill Gates / computers / dancers

_____

3 romantic books / writes / paints / Danielle Steel

_____

4 music / cooks / Andrew Lloyd Webber / composes

_____

5 Gerhard Richter / sings / paints / pictures

_____

6 cooks / Gordon Ramsey / amazing food / plays

_____

7 sings / Placido Domingo / in operas / dances

_____

4 ★★★ Write sentences about famous people or your friends with the words in exercise 1. Write two sentences for each person, one with the noun form and one with the verb form of each word.

My friend Pablo is a very good cook.

He cooks fantastic food for us.

1 _____
_____
2 _____
_____
3 _____
_____
4 _____
_____
5 _____
_____
6 _____
_____

Ability: *can* and *could*

1 ⭐ Complete the table with the words in the box.

> can't   could   play   can   could   ~~can~~
> couldn't   can

Present	✔ I can sing. ✘ He ¹_____ play tennis. ? ²_____ they dance? Yes, they ³_____. / No, they can't.
Past	✔ She ⁴_____ sing. ✘ We couldn't ⁵_____ tennis. ? ⁶_____ they dance? Yes, they could. / No, they ⁷_____.

2 ⭐⭐ Choose the correct words.

I **don't can** / **can't** / **no can** sing.

1 I **can** / **could** / **canned** paint when I was six.
2 We **not can** / **can't** / **don't can** cook.
3 Alisha can **speaks** / **speak** / **speaking** English.
4 He **could** / **could to** / **coulds** dance.
5 She **didn't could** / **could no** / **couldn't** swim.
6 Marek **can to** / **can** / **cans** play tennis.

3 ⭐⭐ Study the table. Write affirmative and negative sentences about the past and the present.

	Past	Present
I	dance when I was little ✘	write Japanese ✘
you		speak German ✔
he		play tennis ✘
she	paint pictures when she was four ✔	
we	cook when we were children ✘	
they		program a computer ✔

I couldn't dance when I was little.

1 _____
2 _____
3 _____
4 _____
5 _____
6 _____

4 ⭐⭐⭐ Make sentences with *can* / *can't*, *could* / *couldn't* and some of the words in the boxes.

People
I   My mum / dad   My friend (name) My grandparents

Verbs
sing   cook   run   dance   drive   swim   play speak

Other words
the guitar   5 km   very well   a car   French tennis   great food

Time expressions
now   last year   in 1995 when he / she was young

I couldn't drive a car when I was young.

1 _____
2 _____
3 _____
4 _____
5 _____
6 _____

Questions with *How ... ?*

5 ⭐⭐ Complete the questions with *how* and the words in the box. Then match questions 1–6 with answers a–f.

> tall   strict   often   ~~far~~   much   many

1 ___How far___ can you swim?   __f__
2 _____ CDs have you got?   _____
3 _____ are your parents?   _____
4 _____ is your brother?   _____
5 _____ water do you drink?   _____
6 _____ do you go shopping?   _____

a I drink a litre of water every day.
b He's one metre seventy-five.
c They aren't very strict.
d one or two times a month.
e I've got about 200.
f I can swim one kilometre.

VOCABULARY ■ Adjectives: qualities

1 ★ Find six more pairs of adjectives with opposite meanings.

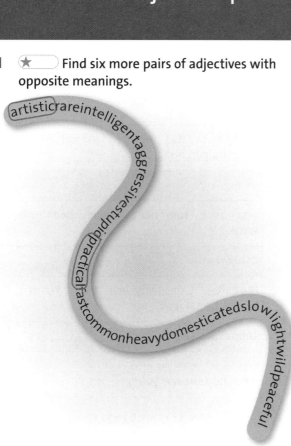

artisticrareintelligentaggressivestupidpracticalfastcommonheavydomesticatedslowlightwildpeaceful

artistic – practical

1 _____
2 _____
3 _____
4 _____
5 _____
6 _____

2 ★★ Complete the sentences with the words in the box.

> light   aggressive   artistic   ~~fast~~   heavy
> intelligent   rare

Horses can run at about fifty kilometres an hour. They're quite _____fast_____.

1 Dolphins are very _____. They can do a lot of clever things.
2 Blue whales are really _____. They weigh about 150,000 kilogrammes.
3 Some people are _____. They can paint beautiful pictures.
4 There are only a few tigers in the world now. They're very _____.
5 Monkeys aren't _____. They don't often fight.
6 Most birds are small and _____, so they can fly easily.

3 ★★ Look at the pictures. Write affirmative and negative sentences with the adjectives.

tigers / fast / slow
Tigers are fast.
They aren't slow.

1 dogs / wild / domesticated
_____
_____
_____

2 dolphins / aggressive / peaceful
_____
_____
_____

3 blue whales / light / heavy
_____
_____
_____

4 chimpanzees / stupid / intelligent
_____
_____
_____

5 rabbits / rare / common
_____
_____
_____

4 ★★★ Write sentences about animals. Use adjectives from exercises 1–3 and *not very*, *quite*, *very* and *really*. Give a reason for your description.

Cats are very common. A lot of people have got a cat.

1 _____
2 _____
3 _____
4 _____
5 _____
6 _____

Comparative and superlative adjectives

1 ★ Choose the correct words to complete the table.

Adjective	Comparative	Superlative
light	_lighter_ than	the ¹_____
big	² _____ than	the biggest
heavy	heavier ³_____	⁴_____
intelligent	⁵_____ than	the most intelligent
good	⁶_____ than	⁷_____ best
bad	worse than	⁸_____

(lighter) / lightest
1 lightest / most light
2 biger / bigger
3 than / that
4 a heaviest / the heaviest
5 intelligenter / more intelligent
6 better / more better
7 more / the
8 the worse / the worst

2 ★★ Complete the sentences with the words in the box.

> than   dangerous   most   more   ~~bigger~~
> the   tallest   best

Dogs are ___bigger___ than cats.

1 Giraffes are the _____ animals in the world.
2 Elephants aren't longer _____ blue whales.
3 Humans are _____ common than tigers.
4 Have chimpanzees got the _____ memory?
5 Dolphins aren't _____ noisiest animals in the sea.
6 Gorillas aren't the _____ aggressive animals.
7 Are humans the most _____ animals in the world?

3 ★★ Write sentences using comparative or superlative adjectives.

cats / light / lions
Cats are lighter than lions.

1 humans / intelligent / gorillas
_____

2 blue whales / big / animals in the world
_____

3 monkeys / heavy / spiders
_____

4 tigers / dangerous / zebras
_____

5 pandas / rare / animals
_____

4 ★★★ Write three comparative and three superlative sentences about yourself and your family. Use the words in the box.

> ~~heavy~~   good   intelligent   artistic   bad
> practical   dangerous

My dad is a lot heavier than my brother, and a bit
heavier than my mum.

1 _____
2 _____
3 _____
4 _____
5 _____
6 _____

should and *must*

5 ★★ Complete the sentences. Use *must / mustn't* or *should / shouldn't* and the correct form of the verbs in brackets.

You __should take__ (take) a break. You look tired.

I __mustn't be__ (be) late. It's my English exam!

1 Frances _____ (stay) up so late at night.
2 In the UK, you _____ (drive) on the left side of the road.
3 You _____ (clean) your teeth more often. They're yellow!
4 We _____ (protect) wild animals if we want them to survive.
5 You _____ (smoke) here. It's against the law.
6 You _____ (buy) that CD. It's great!

Learning at home

In Britain some families feel that learning at home is better than going to school. Home-schooled children can choose when they want to learn. Does this sound more enjoyable than school?

Adrian is a science prodigy and he wants to start university by the age of fourteen. He finds school lessons easier than most children, but making friends more difficult.

At home, he can spend more time on his favourite subjects and is preparing to take many of his exams early. Does he ever take a break? 'Yes,' he says, 'I don't study subjects I'm not interested in.'

Holly's parents weren't happy with the local school, so they made a decision to teach her at home. Her favourite subject is history and she often goes to museums to study. 'I couldn't do that before,' she says. 'This is more interesting than school was.' Her parents are always happy to help her.

Adrian and Holly love learning at home, but some people think that studying at school is more useful because it trains you for adult life. It teaches you to be with people you don't like, but it can also help you to make friends. Are these things more important than lessons? What do you think?

1 ⭐ Read the text. Tick ✔ the correct box.

The writer of the text ...

a ☐ thinks that home-schooling is wrong.

b ☐ says home-schooling is better for everyone.

c ☐ asks the reader to decide if home-schooling is a good idea.

2 ⭐⭐ Read the text again. Match 1–6 with a–f.

1 Some British children don't   _c_

2 Home-schooled children have more   ___

3 Adrian isn't very good at   ___

4 Science lessons at school are   ___

5 Holly's parents chose to   ___

6 School can help you to learn   ___

a making new friends.

b how to make friends.

c go to school.

d very easy for Adrian.

e choice about the subjects they learn.

f teach her at home.

3 ⭐⭐ Read the text again. Complete the sentences with the words in the box.

> likes   university   ~~school~~   learns
> subject   parents

In Britain, people can learn at home or at ___school___.

1 Adrian wants to start _____ when he's 14.

2 He only studies things that he _____.

3 History is Holly's favourite _____.

4 She _____ at home and in museums.

5 Holly's _____ help her when she needs something.

4 ⭐⭐⭐ Write sentences about your experiences of school. What are / were the good and bad things? How is learning at home different? Use the words in the box to help you.

> could(n't)   can('t)   socialize   learn   study
> interesting   enjoyable   parents   subject

At my last school, I couldn't study French,
but now I can study three languages.

1 _____

2 _____

3 _____

4 _____

5 _____

Build your vocabulary

5 ⭐⭐ Complete the sentences with the correct form of the verbs in the box.

> ~~make~~   take   start   make   break

Some children find it very difficult to ___make___ friends.

1 We _____ our exams last summer.

2 Edward's exam results _____ the record for high marks last year.

3 I want to _____ university soon.

4 You need to _____ a decision about the subjects you want to study.

Language point: time expressions

1 ⭐ Choose the correct words.

Swimmer Michael Phelps was born (in) / on 1985.

1 TV chef Jamie Oliver worked at his parents' restaurant **during / for** eight years before he went to catering college.
2 Lady Gaga's first album came out **in / on** August 19th 2008.
3 Actress Emma Watson was famous **by / for** the age of eleven.
4 Mozart started composing music at five years old. A year **late / later**, he played concerts around Europe.
5 Cristiano Ronaldo is **now / for** the highest-paid footballer in the world.
6 Bill Gates started programming computers **in / by** High School.

2 ⭐⭐ Complete the sentences with the correct time expressions.

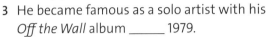

Michael Jackson was born ___on___ 29th August 1958.

1 Jackson was a famous singer and dancer _____ the time he was ten years old.
2 He performed with his brothers in The Jackson Five _____ twenty years.
3 He became famous as a solo artist with his *Off the Wall* album _____ 1979.
4 Three years _____, he made his most successful album, *Thriller*.
5 _____ 25th June 2009, Michael Jackson died at home.

⬤ TASK

Who's the mystery person? Read and find out!

This person was born in ___London___ in 1989. He grew up and went to school there. He became interested ¹_____ by the age of five, and first appeared on TV in ²_____. His life changed in 2001, when his ³_____ appeared in cinemas. This was the first in a series of films which earned him a lot of money. He also won several awards for ⁴_____. In his free time he ⁵_____ the guitar. He's most ⁶_____ his role as Harry Potter, but many people know his ⁷_____ and dramas, too. Who is he? He's ⁸_____.

3 ⭐⭐ Read the information and complete the text. Use one, two or three words.

From: London

Early life: interested in acting from age of five

Career: first TV job 1999; first big film 2001; several Best Actor awards

Plays: guitar

Famous for: Harry Potter role; plays and TV dramas

4 ⭐⭐⭐ Write a biography of a famous person. Put the information into three paragraphs:

1 Where was the person born? Where did he / she grow up?
2 What is the person good at / interested in? What special things did he / she do?
3 What is the person famous for? Who is he / she?

VOCABULARY ● Skills and people

1 Complete the text with the words in the box.

> anything   writer   wrote   painted   lot
> don't

Leonardo da Vinci (1452–1519) is world famous as a wonderful painter. He ¹_____ the most famous picture in the world, the Mona Lisa, around 1505. Many people know a ²_____ about his artwork, but they ³_____ know much about the other things he could do. He was also a brilliant inventor, scientist and a ⁴_____, too. He ⁵_____ all of his thoughts in his notebooks, and we still have some of these today. They contain ideas for a helicopter, solar power, a calculator and a military tank. Da Vinci also studied science, but I don't know ⁶_____ about his writings on this subject.

> **I can say how much I know about a person.**
>
> MY EVALUATION ⬜⬜⬜⬜

READING ● Whizz-kids

2 Match 1–6 with a–f.

1 Some child prodigies don't   ___
2 I talk to my parents before I make   ___
3 We take all of our   ___
4 Usain Bolt broke the   ___
5 Child prodigies often start   ___
6 It's easier to make   ___

a exams in June.
b university very early.
c world record for running 100m.
d take a break from their studies at all.
e friends if you don't move schools a lot.
f big decisions.

> **I can understand a text about child prodigies.**
>
> MY EVALUATION ⬜⬜⬜⬜

LANGUAGE FOCUS ● Ability: *can* and *could*

3 Complete the sentences with *can, can't, could* and *couldn't*.

1 When I was two weeks old, I _____ talk.
2 He _____ play football now.
3 My dog _____ run when it was young, but it's too old now!
4 Elephants _____ fly.
5 We _____ choose how we memorize things.
6 A hundred years ago we _____ chat on the internet!

Questions with *How ... ?*

4 Write questions with words and phrases in the boxes. Then match questions 1–5 with answers a–e.

> ~~How strict~~   How much money   How long
> How old   How far

> was   ~~are~~   can   did   is

> you run   you spend on that bag
> Ella when she got married   a blue whale
> ~~your parents~~

1 <u>How strict are your parents?</u>   <u>d</u>
2 _____ __
3 _____ __
4 _____ __
5 _____ __

a About €100! It was too much!
b She was twenty-seven.
c It's about 25 metres long.
d They're not strict at all.
e Not very far at all – about 1 kilometre.

> **I can talk about past and present abilities.**
>
> MY EVALUATION ⬜⬜⬜⬜

VOCABULARY ■ Adjectives: qualities

5 Complete the sentences with the opposite adjectives.

My brother is artistic,

he isn't practical.

1 Tigers aren't domesticated,

_____

2 My computer desk isn't light,

_____

3 Dogs are common,

_____

4 That joke wasn't intelligent,

_____

5 My favourite songs are slow,

_____

6 Most fish aren't aggressive,

_____

I can describe the qualities of things.

MY EVALUATION ☐☐☐☐

LANGUAGE FOCUS ■ Comparative and superlative adjectives

6 Complete the sentences. Use the comparative or superlative forms of the adjectives and *than* or *the*.

1 African elephants are _____ (big) Indian elephants.

2 Cats are more _____ (common) tigers.

3 I'm _____ (fast) runner at school.

4 Jack can swim _____ (far) Mark.

5 My room is a lot _____ (tidy) my sister's room.

6 These are _____ (expensive) shoes in the shop!

I can use comparative and superlative adjectives.

MY EVALUATION ☐☐☐☐

SPEAKING ■ Choosing a present

7 Number the dialogue in the correct order.

☐ Harry Good idea! Who's it by? Is it by Goya?

☐ Harry Well, I don't know anything about art. But I think this other one's better.

☐ Harry Definitely. The first one's a bit dark.

☐ Harry Dan, is this by Goya?

☐ Rachel I'm not sure. Let's ask Dan. He's into art.

[1] Rachel Look at these posters. I like this one. We should buy it for Mandy's birthday.

☐ Rachel Do you think so?

☐ Dan Yes. I know a bit about his work.

I can compare ideas for a present.

MY EVALUATION ☐☐☐☐

WRITING ■ Biographies

8 Complete the biography with the words in the box.

now   later   on   for   by   in

Leonardo DiCaprio was born [1]_____ November 11th 1974, to a German mother and an Italian American father. His parents were divorced [2]_____ the time Leo was a year old. He grew up in Los Angeles, USA, and [3]_____ 1990, aged just 16, he got his first TV acting job. Two years [4]_____ , he acted in his first film, *This Boy's Life*. DiCaprio worked as a film actor [5]_____ just five years before becoming a superstar, when he played Jack Dawson in *Titanic*. The film won 11 Oscars, and is one of the most successful movies of all time. He is [6]_____ a big celebrity, and works as an actor, a film producer, and for many charities.

I can write a biography of a person.

MY EVALUATION ☐☐☐☐

VOCABULARY ● Time and numbers

1 ⭐ Write the numbers as words.

4,000,000,000
four billion

4 6,000,000
_____

1 7th October
_____
_____

5 ½
_____

2 0
_____

6 ¼
_____

3 3,958
_____
_____
_____
_____

7 802
_____
_____
_____

2 ⭐⭐ Correct the words in **bold** in the sentences.

There are a hundred years in a ~~decade~~.
century

1 There are twelve **weeks** in a year.
_____

2 There are fifty-two **days** in a year.
_____

3 There are ten **minutes** in a decade.
_____

4 There are usually 365 **centuries** in a year.
_____

5 There are twenty-four **minutes** in a day.
_____

6 There are ten years in a **millennium**.
_____

7 There are sixty **seconds** in an hour.
_____

8 There are sixty **months** in a minute.
_____

3 ⭐⭐ Complete the dialogues with the words in the box.

| a quarter ~~a decade~~ a half a century |
| a couple a few a dozen |

Rebecca Was your mum born in the 1960s?
Amy No, in the 1970s. **A decade** later.
1 James Cut the chocolate cake into four pieces.
   Freddie Yes, we can have _____ each.
2 Jay What's 50% as a fraction?
   Callum It's _____.
3 Katie How many eggs do we need?
   Max We need two boxes of six eggs, so that's _____ eggs.
4 Rosa Did your dad go to London for a week?
   Morgan No, only for _____ days.
5 Charlie I bought _____ of apples to eat.
   Jack Great. That's one for me and one for you.
6 Rita My great grandfather was born in 1906.
   Paula Wow, that's over _____ ago.

4 ⭐⭐⭐ Complete the text with time and number words.

People think Aborigines started living in Australia more than forty _thousand years_ ago.

The English explorer Captain Cook visited Australia in the eighteenth ¹_____.

Australia is enormous and it takes fifty hours to drive non-stop from Sydney to Perth. That's more than two ²_____! It takes five ³_____ to fly from Sydney to Perth. There are around twenty-one ⁴_____ people in Australia. The hottest ⁵_____ in Australia are December, January and February. There was a big party in Sydney on 31st December 1999, to celebrate the new ⁶_____. In 2000, Sydney was the home of the Olympic Games for two ⁷_____.

LANGUAGE FOCUS ◼ will, won't

6

1 ⭐ Choose the correct words to complete the table.

Affirmative		
I / you / he / she/ it / we / they	will (full form) ___'ll___ (short form)	³_____ late. study tonight.

Negative		
I / you / he / she/ it / we / they	¹_____ (full form) ²_____ (short form)	⁴_____ tennis. see that film.

Questions and answers	
⁵_____ Mikhail be there?	Yes, he will. / No, he won't.
When will you be 16?	I ⁶_____ be 16 next May.

(’ll) / 's
1 don't will / will not
2 won't / wont
3 to be / be
4 play / playing
5 Does / Will
6 'll / 'm

2 ⭐⭐ Write questions with *will*. Then match questions 1–6 with answers a–f.

1 the next American president / be / a woman?
   Will the next American president be a woman? b

2 who / be / the best racing driver / next year
   _____

3 Brazil / win / the next football World Cup
   _____

4 what / children / study / in the future
   _____

5 Lady Gaga / have / a number one record next year
   _____

6 where / people / live / in the next millennium
   _____

a I think it'll be computer programming.
b No, I reckon it'll be a man again.
c Yes, I bet she will. She's a great singer.
d Lewis Hamilton, maybe.
e I don't know. Maybe in houses under the sea!
f Yes, I'm pretty sure they will.

3 ⭐⭐ Choose the correct words.

Venus Williams will **winning** / (win) / **to win** this match.

1 Don't worry! Your teacher **not will** / **don't will** / **won't** be angry.
2 Mike **buys** / **will to buy** / **will buy** a new car next year.
3 I think it **will** / **wills** / **doesn't** rain later.
4 **You will** / **Will you** / **Do you** travel a lot in the future?
5 I'm feeling ill. I **am not** / **don't** / **won't** go to the party tomorrow.
6 Will you be there tomorrow? Yes, **I'll** / **I will** / **will**.

4 ⭐⭐⭐ Make guesses about the future with the words in the boxes and your own ideas. Use *will* and *won't*.

> I reckon that   I bet that
> I'm pretty sure that   I imagine that

> get married   win   lose   move to   visit
> have a baby   become   write   buy

Actors and celebrities
I bet that Katie Holmes
and Tom Cruise will have
another baby.
Sports stars and teams
_____
_____
_____
_____

Pop stars and musicians
_____
_____
_____
_____
_____

People you know
_____
_____
_____
_____
_____

1 ⭐ Find five more pairs of personality adjectives with opposite meanings.

outgoing mean impatient easygoing shy serious generous arrogant patient modest funny moody

outgoing – shy	3	_____
1 _____	4	_____
2 _____	5	_____

2 ⭐⭐ Complete the sentences with suitable personality adjectives.

A ____shy____ person is someone who feels nervous when they meet new people.

1 A _____ person is someone who always smiles at people and says hello.

2 An _____ person is someone who doesn't have many original ideas.

3 An _____ person is someone who wants to get a good job in the future.

4 A _____ person is someone who is good at making things with their hands.

5 A _____ person doesn't like giving things to other people.

6 An _____ person is someone who gets angry when they have to wait for a long time.

7 A _____ person is someone who often feels sad and angry.

8 A _____ person is someone who thinks about the bad things in the world.

9 An _____ person is someone who is relaxed and doesn't often get angry.

3 ⭐⭐ Complete the text with the words in the box.

moody ~~serious~~ positive shy
ambitious generous friendly

What's your personality?

Erin, 13
I think I'm a ___serious___ person. At school I study hard and I always do my homework. I'm also ¹_____ – I want to be a doctor in the future. My teachers sometimes think I'm ²_____, because I don't ask many questions and I don't like talking in front of the class. But I'm very ³_____ with the girls at school and we always laugh and chat in the morning.

Rees, 14
Everybody says I'm a very ⁴_____ person – I always give my friends nice presents and I buy flowers for my mum on her birthday. I don't like negative people. I always try to see the good things in the world because I want to be a ⁵_____ person. But I'm not happy all the time! My dad says I'm ⁶_____ because I sometimes feel bad when I get up, but after breakfast I'm happy again!

4 ⭐⭐⭐ Write sentences about two people you know. Use adjectives to describe their personality.

My teacher is really patient with everybody.

He's also very positive and he always says 'Well done!'

1 _____
_____
_____

2 _____
_____
_____

First conditional

1 ★ Complete the table with the words in the box.

> will   see   tell   'll   if   arrives   miss
> rains   won't

	If	Present tense +,	Future tense
✔	__If__	I see Julieta,	I'll ¹_____ her the news.
✗	If	it ²_____,	we won't have a picnic.
?	If	Mike arrives late,	³_____ he miss the bus?

	Future tense	If	Present tense
✔	I ⁴_____ tell Julieta the news	if	I ⁵_____ her.
✗	We ⁶_____ have a picnic	if	it rains.
?	Will Mike ⁷_____ the bus	if	he ⁸_____ late?

2 ★★ Complete the sentences using the correct form of the verbs in brackets.

If you ___don't go___ (not go) to bed, you'll be tired.

1 If James phones you, what _____ (you / say) to him?
2 Marie _____ (be) cross if we're late for her party.
3 What will you do if you _____ (not pass) your exams?
4 If I _____ (see) the new Black Eyed Peas CD in the shops, I'll buy it.
5 Cara _____ (not become) a famous singer if she doesn't practise!
6 If they train every day, they _____ (win) the match.
7 If it _____ (snow) today, we won't go for a walk.
8 I won't talk to Peter if he _____ (be) moody again today.

3 ★★★ Complete the sentences with your ideas. Use the first conditional.

If we all study very hard, _we'll do well in_ _our exams._

1 I'll phone my best friend today if _____ _____.
2 My dad won't give me any money if _____ _____.
3 If I don't tidy my room this evening, _____ _____.
4 If my favourite team wins the match, _____ _____.
5 Will you still love me if _____ _____.
6 She won't pass her exams if _____ _____.

Expressing probability

4 ★★ Rewrite the sentences. Put the words in brackets in the correct place.

I'll see you in an hour or two. (probably)
I'll probably see you in an hour or two.

1 Usain Bolt will continue to be the fastest runner for a long time. (probably)
_____
_____

2 We won't have time to go to the museum. (definitely)
_____
_____

3 If the weather is terrible, we won't visit the seaside. (probably)
_____
_____

4 I'll be ill if we don't stop soon. (probably)
_____
_____

5 If there isn't enough food, the tourists will complain. (definitely)
_____
_____

1 ★ Read the text. Tick ✔ the correct box.

The text is about ...

a ☐ the fact that many sports stars have lots of good luck.

b ☐ the beliefs that sports stars have about what will give them good or bad luck.

c ☐ the fact that successful sports people are more superstitious than other people.

Sports stars and their superstitions

If you think about famous sports stars, you'll see that they sometimes wear special clothes for important matches. For example, the American golfer Tiger Woods always wears red and black clothes for the last game of a tournament. Why do people do this? They're superstitious, of course. Some players have the fear that if they don't wear their 'lucky' clothes, they won't be so successful.

Many footballers are famous for their superstitions. Spanish star Fernando Torres believes the number three will bring him good fortune. Before a match he always puts out three football shirts and three pairs of shorts, socks and boots. He doesn't wear all three while he is playing, however!

Superstitions are important in tennis too. When the Croatian tennis champion Goran Ivanisevic played at Wimbledon he always ate the same dinner at the same restaurant every night, and finished the meal with ice cream. And when American tennis star Serena Williams plays in a tournament, she always uses the same shower. She's also got three or four lucky dresses.

What do you think? Will special clothes or rituals bring luck and prosperity? If your favourite team puts on lucky shorts, will they definitely win, or is it just a superstition?

2 ★★ Read the text again. Write the person.

Who ...

... puts out more than one shirt before a match?

<u>Fernando Torres</u>

1 ... always wears clothes in a special colour?

_____

2 ... went to the same restaurant every night?

_____

3 ... thinks the number three is lucky?

_____

4 ... goes in the same shower?

_____

3 ★★★ Answer the questions. Write complete sentences.

What will you see if you look carefully at your favourite sports stars?

<u>They sometimes wear special clothes for important</u>
<u>matches.</u>

1 When does Tiger Woods wear red and black clothes?

_____

2 Why do players sometimes wear special things?

_____

3 What does Fernando Torres put out before a match?

_____

4 Which stars have got a superstition that is not related to clothes?

_____

Build your vocabulary

4 ★★ Complete the sentences with the words in the box.

~~lucky~~   superstition   superstitious   fear

In the UK people say that a black cat is ____<u>lucky</u>____.

1 My little sister has a _____ of the dark, so she sleeps with the light on.

2 Many sports stars are very _____ about the clothes they wear.

3 I've got a _____: I always use the same pen in my exams.

1 ★ Choose the correct words.

Everybody **understand** / **understands** the questions in the survey.

1 Most people **believe** / **believes** that children will be taller in the next century.
2 Everybody **has** / **have** got an opinion about the future.
3 One or two people **want** / **wants** to visit a different planet.
4 Some people **think** / **thinks** that there will be more deserts in the future.
5 Nobody **know** / **knows** the answer to the problem.
6 More than half of us **is** / **are** very worried about the future.
7 A lot of people **believe** / **believes** we will soon have holidays in space.

Language point: Expressing quantity

2 ★★ Complete the sentences with the words in the box.

> of   nobody   some of us   ~~most~~
> everybody   people   or

___Most___ people think the population will be much bigger.

1 _____ believes there will be environmental problems.
2 One _____ two students enjoy reading newspaper articles about the future.
3 _____ thinks the future will be exactly the same as now.
4 Most _____ the class talk to their friends about the future of the planet.
5 _____ watch programmes about wild animals.
6 Most _____ are worried about the future for tigers.

◘ TASK

3 ★★ Read the information and complete the email. Use *will* in the sentences.

> **Everybody thinks:** *Big Brother* / become / less popular
>
> **Half of us reckon:** we / get / more / TV / channels
>
> **Most people say:** there / be / more sport on TV
>
> **Some boys think:** there / be / a lot more football
>
> **One or two people think:** we / probably / have / better programmes for teenagers
>
> **The rest of us say:** there / be / lots more adverts!
>
> **Everybody says:** children / definitely / watch / more TV in the future

4 ★★★ Imagine you and your friends talked about the future of pop music, film or sports stars. Write an email. Use the text in exercise 3 to help you.

Delete Reply Reply All Forward New Mailboxes Get Mail   Q▾ From   Search Mailbox

Hi, Becky!

How's your new school? Do you like your teachers?

After class yesterday we went to the park with our friends – Cassie, Kate, James, Jack and all the others. There were eight of us. We started chatting about the future of TV programmes and we talked for more than an hour! _Everybody thinks that Big Brother will become less popular_. Kate and I prefer *The X Factor*. It's much more exciting! Half of us reckon that ¹_____. Most people say that ²_____. And some boys think that ³_____.Oh, dear! I hate football! ⁴_____ better programmes for teenagers. But I'm not sure about this. The rest of us say ⁵_____ – how boring! Everybody says ⁶_____ more TV in the future. What do you think?

Love,

Lisa

VOCABULARY ■ Time and numbers

1 Complete the number and time words. What is the hidden word?

1 seven _____ = one week
2 sixty _____ in an hour
3 one hundred years in a _____
4 2013 = two _____ and thirteen
5 twelve = a _____
6 18th

The hidden word is _____.

I can use a wide variety of numbers and times.
MY EVALUATION ☐☐☐☐

READING ■ Superstitions

2 Choose the correct words.

1 Cheri was very **fortune / lucky** to win the lottery.
2 I have a big **fear / superstition** of spiders. I really hate them!
3 Do you believe that the number thirteen is **superstitious / unlucky**?
4 There are lots of **superstitious / superstitions** about weddings.
5 I'm not at all **superstitious / superstition**. I think we make our own luck.

I can understand a text about numbers.
MY EVALUATION ☐☐☐☐

LANGUAGE FOCUS ■ will, won't

3 Complete the sentences with 'll / will (✔) or won't (✗) and the verbs in the box.

climb   be   rain   eat   read   spend

1 We _____ on holiday in Mexico next month. ✔
2 I _____ magazines on the beach all day. ✗
3 Maria _____ a lot of Mexican food. ✔
4 Adrian _____ a lot of money. ✔
5 It _____ tomorrow. ✗
6 Daniel and Anna _____ up a mountain. ✗

I can make predictions using will and won't.
MY EVALUATION ☐☐☐☐

VOCABULARY ■ Adjectives: characteristics

4 Replace the underlined adjectives with their opposites.

1 Nina isn't very shy. She's always nervous about new social situations. _____
2 My uncle is a very patient driver. He never waits for anyone. _____
3 Gita is totally ambitious. She doesn't care what job she gets. _____
4 My little sister is a bit easy-going when she's tired. Watch out! _____
5 Callum isn't very arrogant about his achievements. He never stops talking about them! _____
6 My Dad is really serious. He's always telling jokes. _____

I can talk about people's personality.
MY EVALUATION ☐☐☐☐

LANGUAGE FOCUS ■ First conditional

5 Complete the sentences with the correct form of the verbs.

1 If we _____ (do) our homework, the teacher _____ (be) happy.
2 If you _____ (not listen), you _____ (not understand) the question.
3 He _____ (study) English if he _____ (visit) Australia.
4 You _____ (not pass) the exam if you _____ (not study) every day.
5 _____ (we / play) tennis tomorrow if it _____ (be) sunny?
6 If it _____ (rain) tomorrow, where _____ (we / go)?

> **I can talk about conditions and their results.**
> MY EVALUATION ☐☐☐☐

SPEAKING ■ A future survey

6 Choose the correct words.

Cara It's Sophie's birthday party next week. I think ¹**it'll be / it's** great.
Jack Yeah, I ²**agree / am agree**. Sophie's parties are always brilliant. ³**Are / Do** you think she'll invite you?
Cara Yes, definitely. We're best friends. What ⁴**for / about** you? Do you want to go?
Jack If she invites you, she'll probably ask me.
Cara Oh, why's ⁵**that / it**, Jack?
Jack Because she thinks we're going out together!
Cara Really? Who told her that? Let ⁶**I / me** think. Was it *you*?
Jack Er … Sorry Cara. If I go to the party, I'll see Fran, and I really like her.
Cara Yeah, but she won't talk to you, if she thinks *we're* going out!
Jack Oh! I didn't think of that!

> **I can speak about the future.**
> MY EVALUATION ☐☐☐☐

WRITING ■ A report on a survey

7 Match sentence halves 1–6 with a–f.

1 We've got our exams next year. Nobody ___
2 We all hate homework, but most ___
3 More than ___
4 We all like shopping, but a ___
5 One or two people ___
6 School ends in two weeks, and everybody ___

a half of the students in my class are boys.
b lot of us can't afford it!
c want to become doctors in the future.
d is really excited about summer.
e thinks that school will be easier.
f of us do it on time.

> **I can write a report about a survey.**
> MY EVALUATION ☐☐☐☐

7 Sport for all

VOCABULARY ● People in sport

1 ★ **Correct the words.**

~~referee~~

champion

1 champion

j_____

2 supporter

t_____

3 finalist

r_____

4 captain

s_____

5 manager

l_____

2 ★★ **Complete the sentences.**

> loser sponsor ~~champion~~ referee
> journalist trainer supporter

The winner of a sports competition is the
champion .

1 A _____ is a company which gives
money to a sports team.

2 A _____ works for a newspaper,
magazine or TV company.

3 When you want a team or sportsperson to
win, you're a _____ .

4 When you don't win a game, you're the
_____ .

5 A _____ controls the game and makes
sure all the players follow the rules.

6 A _____ teaches sportspeople or
teams to do their sport better.

3 ★★ **Do the _Famous people in sport_ quiz.
Choose the correct answers.**

Famous people in sport

David Beckham was _____ of the English
football team from 2000 to 2006.
  a sponsor **b** (captain) **c** supporter

1 Roger Federer was a _____ at the 2008
  Wimbledon Tennis Championship.
  a finalist **b** supporter **c** referee

2 Runner Usain Bolt has a _____ who
  organizes his training and competitions.
  a champion **b** manager **c** journalist

3 When Roman Abramovich bought Chelsea
  Football Club, he became its _____ .
  a captain **b** trainer **c** owner

4 For many years, the Williams sisters' father
  was their tennis _____ .
  a trainer **b** finalist **c** champion

5 The sports clothes company Reebok is a big
  _____ of many sports.
  a trainer **b** manager **c** sponsor

4 ★★★ **Complete the sports report with words
from exercises 1–3.**

It's half-time here in the cup final and the
score is 2–2. A.C City were ¹_____ s
last year too, but they were the
²_____ s. Can they win this time?
The other team, Thorpe United, are having
an amazing season. About 30,000 of their
³_____ are here today, cheering
them on. Thorpe's ⁴_____ , Jimmy
Jones, bought some great new players
last year. But where did all the money
come from? Several sports ⁵_____ s
reported recently that maybe Thorpe got a
new ⁶_____ last month, the Russian
millionaire Igor Poliakov. Nobody is sure,
but the team is certainly a lot richer than it
was before.

Imperatives

1 ★★ Give advice to a football player. Make affirmative and negative imperatives.

> get ~~buy~~ listen watch eat go ~~have~~

___Have___ a quiet evening tonight.

___Don't buy___ any junk food.

1 _____ some pasta for dinner.
2 _____ to bed too late.
3 _____ Romanov. You can learn a lot from him.
4 _____ to the team captain.
5 _____ angry with the referee.

be going to: affirmative and negative

2 ★ Complete the table with the words in the box.

> send 's aren't 'm play not

Affirmative			
Subject	***be***	***going to***	**Verb**
I	'm		swim.
he / she / it	¹_____		
we / you / they	're		⁴_____
Negative		going to	tennis.
Subject	***be***		⁵_____
I	'm ²_____		an email.
he / she / it	isn't		
we / you / they	³_____		get up.

3 ★★ Order the words to make sentences. There is one extra word in each sentence.

owner / to / the / look / going / for / are / a / new / manager / is
The owner is going to look for a new manager.

1 I'm / to / don't / tomorrow / going / play / not / football /
_____

2 team / has / the / have / going / to / new / sponsors / is
_____

3 not / we / going / to / the / match / watch / aren't / tennis
_____

4 he / be / aren't / going / to / the / captain next / year / isn't
_____

5 play / basketball / aren't / the / to / you / going / in / not / team
_____

6 to / pay / are / competition / the / going / sponsors / be / for / the
_____

will and *be going to*

4 ★★ Complete the sentences using the correct from of the verbs for predictions and plans. Use *will* and *be going to*.

I think ___she'll win___ (win) the championship next year.

We ___aren't going to watch___ (not watch) the game on TV.

1 I _____ (speak) to the journalist now.
2 Maybe the manager _____ (be) angry.
3 The finalists _____ (practise) before the match.
4 I think you _____ (find) a new sponsor.
5 Maybe he _____ (not buy) any players.
6 She _____ (go) to bed early tonight.

5 ★★★ Write about your plans and predictions for the future. Use *will* and *be going to* and the ideas in the box.

	Ideas	Time expressions
Plans	see friends / dentist take exam / test visit cousins / museum / Paris	next Tuesday / week / month / year in May / October on Wednesday at half past eight tonight
Predictions	celebrities your ambitions technology / computers	one day in the future after school / university

I'm going to visit my cousins next week.

I think I'll be famous one day.

1 _____
2 _____
3 _____
4 _____
5 _____
6 _____

1 ⭐ Use the words in the boxes to label the pictures.

> golf cycling skiing rugby ~~football~~
> tennis swimming table tennis

> ~~stadium~~ player trophy fan match
> champion team instructor

football stadium   1 _____

2 _____   3 _____

4 _____   5 _____

6 _____   7 _____

2 ⭐⭐ Complete the crossword.

1 a competition where the fastest person wins
2 a place where you play football or rugby
3 a group of players
4 a sports game between two players or groups of players
5 the winners of a tournament get this
6 a large building where people come to see sports events
7 the time of year when you play a sport
8 the people who support a group of players
9 a sports person who wins big competitions

3 ⭐⭐ Complete the sentences with the words in the box.

> team ~~trophy~~ tournament
> competition instructor match season

The FIFA World Cup is a ___trophy___ made of gold.

1 There are normally five players on court for each basketball _____.
2 My team is going to play a rugby _____ today.
3 I won a _____ in a magazine. I got tickets for a football match.
4 My skiing _____ teaches me every day.
5 The football _____ is from August until May.
6 There are a lot of matches in a tennis _____.

4 Write a sports quiz. Use some of the compound nouns from exercises 1–3 and the words in the box. Can you find the answers on the internet?

> ~~largest~~ longest most expensive best
> oldest most successful fastest

What's the largest football stadium in the UK?

1 _____
2 _____
3 _____
4 _____
5 _____
6 _____

be going to: questions

1 ⭐ Complete the table with the words in the box.

> aren't   he   ~~am~~   he   's   going   are

(Question word)	*be*	Subject	*going to*	Verb
Where When	<u>Am</u> Is ² _____	I ¹ _____ they	going to	swim? play? read? eat?

Answers

Yes, he is. / No, ³ _____ isn't.
Yes, they are. / No, they ⁴ _____.
You're ⁵ _____ to swim at 5pm.
He ⁶ _____ going to play at the stadium.

2 ⭐⭐ Write questions with *be going to*. Then write the answers.

they / lose ✗

<u>Are they going to lose? No, they aren't.</u>

1 where / you / practise (at the athletics stadium)

_____
_____
_____

2 we / watch / the match ✓

_____
_____

3 what time / it / start (at two o'clock)

_____
_____

4 who / she / support (Bayern Munich)

_____
_____
_____

5 they / sponsor / the team ✗

_____
_____

6 you / buy / a ticket ✓

_____
_____

7 when / he / play (on Tuesday)

_____
_____
_____

3 ⭐⭐⭐ Rafael Nadal is going to play in a tennis match tomorrow. Write interview questions using *be going to*.

<u>Are you going to eat a big meal</u>
<u>before the match?</u>

1 Are _____?
2 Is _____?
3 Are _____?
4 When _____?
5 What _____?
6 Where _____?

Present continuous for future arrangements

4 ⭐⭐ Complete the dialogue about future arrangements using the present continuous.

Jenny <u>What are you doing</u> (you / do)
<u>this summer?</u>

Matt ¹ _____ (I / not do) anything special. What about you?

Jenny ² _____ (we / fly) to London to watch a tennis tournament with our English cousins.

Matt ³ _____ (you / meet) them there?

Jenny Yes. ⁴ _____ (we / spend) a week with them, then ⁵ _____ (we / go) to the seaside.

Indefinite pronouns

5 ⭐⭐ Complete the sentences with the words in the box.

> ~~someone~~   anyone   anything
> something   somewhere   someone

Can you answer the phone? <u>Someone</u>'s calling.

1 Our manager wants to buy new players, but we can't afford _____ good!

2 We need _____ to play football. The park is too full of people.

3 _____ stole the tournament trophy. We don't know who did it.

4 Did you win _____ important last year?
No, we haven't got any trophies.

5 Gallagher has _____ special that makes him a champion.

A rising star of table tennis

1 (★) Read the text. Tick ✔ the correct box.

The text is about …

1 ☐ how sport can change your life.
2 ☐ how to improve at table tennis.
3 ☐ one player's plans and ambitions.

A Damien Short grew up in a poor part of London, where there was a lot of crime and other problems. But today Damien is a champion and he competes in international tournaments. So what happened to change his situation? He became very good at table tennis! Sporting talent is in Damien's family. His brother is a motorbike racing champion!

B Now Damien trains at the National Table Tennis Academy in Nottingham, and he plays for the British team. His big ambition is to win a gold medal at the next Olympics. 'I know I'll do well there,' he says. 'I'm going to work hard every day, to make sure I'll be in great condition for the games.'

C Damien's training is already very intensive. Next week, he's playing against the Indian national team. And later this year, he's going on a training tour of China, the world's top table tennis nation. 'China will be amazing,' says Damien. 'Millions of people support the national team, and the crowds at tournaments are enormous. The atmosphere is really exciting for the competitors. This trip will be a big learning experience for me.'

D Damien says that kids should play more sport. 'Have a go at something new,' he suggests. 'You've got nothing to lose, and you never know – it could change your life!'

2 (★★) Read the text again. Match questions 1–3 with three of the paragraphs A–D.

1 What is Damien going to do next? _C_
2 What advice has he got for people? _____
3 How did sport change Damien's life? _____

3 (★★) Read the text again. Correct the sentences.

Damien lived in a rich part of London.
Damien lived in a poor part of London.

1 He organizes international tournaments.
_____

2 Damien does his training in London.
_____

3 His biggest aim is to win the world championship.
_____

4 Damien will train four times a week.
_____

4 (★★★) Answer the questions. Write complete sentences.

Did Damien grow up in a nice place?
No, he didn't. It was poor and there was a lot of
crime and other problems.

1 Why did things change for Damien?
_____

2 Why does Damien live in Nottingham now?
_____

3 What does he want to do at the next Olympics?
_____

4 What is special about China?
_____

Build your vocabulary

5 (★★) Complete the sentences with the words in the box.

> have a go   racing   atmosphere
> competed   situation   ~~support~~

Which football team do you _support_ ?
Juventus – they're fantastic!

1 Our team is in a terrible _____.
We lost all our games last month.
2 _____ at basketball! Maybe you'll like it.
3 Fran was a professional player and she _____ in international competitions.
4 It's match-point in the tennis final, and the _____ here is very exciting.
5 I don't like motor _____. It's boring!

WRITING ■ A formal letter

7

Language point: Layout and language in a formal letter

1 ★ Complete the letter with the words in the box.

> 12 Althorp Road   14th November
> James Goodwin   Manager
> Sir or Madam

2 ★★ Correct mistakes a–i in the letter.

a _Dear_ ____
b ____
c ____
d ____
e ____
f ____
g ____
h ____
i ____

<u>12 Althorp Road</u>
Bristol, England
¹____

(a) Dears ²____,

I am the manager of an athletics club in Bristol, England. The name of the club is Star Athletes. I am (b) write to you because we are planning a tournament and we are looking for sponsors.

The tournament will take place (c) on April. Teams and fans from four countries (d) going to be in Bristol for this event and I think that it (e) will to be good publicity for your company.

Please (f) contacting me if you are interested in sponsoring us, or if you (g) needs any more information.

I look forward to (h) hear from you.

(i) Your faithfully

³____,

⁴____

○ TASK

3 ★★ You are going to write a formal letter to a photographer. Your letter should have a paragraph for each of the notes a–c. Number them in the order you should include them in your letter.

a ☐ Please contact me.
b ☐ Captain / club name. Looking for a photographer to take pictures of cycling team for new club brochure.
c ☐ Club will send brochure to a lot of schools / good publicity.

4 ★★★ Write the letter to the photographer. Use the writing guide and the information in exercise 3.

Hotwheels Cycling Team
Greenbank Road
Exeter, England
28th March

Dear Sir or Madam,

Paragraph 1:
____
____

Paragraph 2:
____
____

Paragraph 3:
____
____

Yours faithfully,

Rachel Brown

Captain

VOCABULARY ● People in sport

1   Complete the sentences with the words in the box.

> referee   journalist   sponsor's   players   finalists   supporters

1   Make some shirts with the _____ name on them.
2   The _____ are the same two teams as last year.
3   Players shouldn't argue with the _____!
4   The manager has bought some new _____ for next season.
5   The _____ cheered loudly when Rooney scored a goal.
6   Ask the _____ to organize an interview for Saturday's newspaper.

> **I can make suggestions about sport.**
>
> MY EVALUATION   ◻◻◻◻

READING ● Women in sports

2   Match sentence halves 1–6 with a–f.

1   I'd love to have   _____
2   The atmosphere at   _____
3   I don't normally support   _____
4   How often do you compete   _____
5   Ferrari are in the lead but   _____
6   I really love watching   _____

a   motorbike racing. How about you?
b   this driver, but he's performing brilliantly.
c   the situation will probably change.
d   a go at driving a Formula 1 car.
e   in international races?
f   big races is very exciting.

> **I can understand an interview.**
>
> MY EVALUATION   ◻◻◻◻

LANGUAGE FOCUS ● *be going to*

3   Write affirmative ✓ and negative ✗ sentences with *be going to*.

1   Raoul / play / in a big tournament next week ✓
   _____
   _____
2   we / get / tickets for the final ✗
   _____
   _____
3   they / do / some training today ✓
   _____
   _____
4   Alfie / find / a sponsor for the team ✗
   _____
   _____
5   I / have / a rest from competitions ✓
   _____
   _____
6   Rio Ferdinand / move / to a new team next season ✗
   _____
   _____

will and *be going to*

4   Complete the sentences.

1   He _____ (watch) the match at 1 o'clock.
2   He believes they _____ (win) tomorrow.
3   They _____ (play) the game on Sunday at 2.30.
4   I think you _____ (feel) better in the morning.
5   Maybe I _____ (not need) a new sponsor.
6   She _____ (not talk) to the journalist today because she's busy.

> **I can talk about plans and predictions.**
>
> MY EVALUATION   ◻◻◻◻

VOCABULARY ● Compound nouns: sports

5 Match 1–6 with a–f.

1 Wimbledon
2 September to May
3 The Giro d'Italia
4 The FIFA World Cup
5 Usain Bolt
6 The Los Angeles Lakers

a football trophy
b basketball team
c athletic champion
d cycling race
e rugby season
f tennis tournament

> **I can talk about sport.**
>
> MY EVALUATION ☐☐☐☐

LANGUAGE FOCUS ● be going to: questions

6 Write questions and short answers with *be going to*.

1 Meena / leave the party (yes)

_____

2 you / have a holiday this year (no)

_____

3 Clara and Maria / play tennis next week (yes)

_____

4 you / support the same team next year (no)

_____

5 Jenna / try skiing (yes)

_____

6 we / play a match tomorrow (no)

_____

Present continuous for future arrangements

7 Choose the correct words.

1 I **'m seeing** / **'m see** my friend tomorrow.
2 Are you **going** / **go** to New York this year?
3 They **aren't** / **don't** inviting many people.
4 We're **stay** / **staying** at home this Christmas.
5 He's **coming** / **going to coming** home now.

> **I can talk about future arrangements.**
>
> MY EVALUATION ☐☐☐☐

SPEAKING ● Making plans and arrangements

8 Read the dialogue and choose the correct words.

Sam   Hi Dan. Are you doing ¹**something** / **anything** on Saturday?

Dan   Oh, hi Sam. No, ²**anything** / **nothing** special. What ³**are** / **do** you up to?

Sam   ⁴**I'm going** / **I'll go** to a football match, if you're ⁵**interesting** / **interested**.

Dan   Great. I'd love to come! Is it on ⁶**anywhere** / **anything** local?

Sam   Yes, it's at the City Stadium at 2 p.m.

Dan   ⁷**Do** / **Shall** I meet you outside?

Sam   Yeah, great. See ⁸**you** / **us** then.

> **I can invite a friend to a sports event.**
>
> MY EVALUATION ☐☐☐☐

WRITING ● A formal letter

9 Number the items in the correct order for a formal letter.

☐ Yours faithfully
☐ Address
☐ We will need …
☐ Your name
☐ Dear Sir / Madam
☐ Your position (manager, etc.)
☐ I am writing to …
☐ I look forward to hearing from you.

> **I can write a letter to ask for sponsors.**
>
> MY EVALUATION ☐☐☐☐

VOCABULARY ■ Feelings

1 ⭐ Complete the crossword.

```
            ¹
        ²
    ³F  O  N  D
                              ⁵
    ⁴
        ⁶
    ⁷
        ⁸
```

Across

3 Bruno is _fond_ of animals, so he wants to become a farmer.

4 Tito is really _____ about his exams next week.

6 I'm not very _____ about climbing this mountain because I don't like high places.

7 We're all _____ in IT and website design, so we're going to start an after-school computer club.

8 Are you _____ of spiders?

Down

1 I'm not _____ about this English test. It'll be easy!

2 Lenka is very _____ about the skiing trip. She really wants to go.

5 Sam's really _____ at swimming. He trains every day.

2 ⭐⭐ Write the correct prepositions.

scared __of__ means you are frightened of something

1 enthusiastic _____ is similar to interested _____

2 bad _____ is the opposite of good _____

3 stressed out _____ = worried _____

4 keen _____ means you really like something

3 ⭐⭐ Complete the text with the words in the box.

> enthusiastic of ~~interested~~ stressed worried at in

Penfriend page

My name's Ethan and I'm __interested__ in finding a penfriend. I'm 15 and I live in Sheffield in the north of England. My family are very fond ¹_____ travelling, and we've been to Spain, Portugal, Russia and France. Next year, we're going to Italy.

I'm really ²_____ about studying languages. I speak Spanish, French and German, although I'm not very good ³_____ German. I want to practise my language with my new penfriend – I'm not really ⁴_____ about making mistakes.

Everybody in my family loves football and our favourite team is Sheffield United. We're all a bit ⁵_____ out about the club's future now, because they've had a terrible season.

What about you? Are you interested ⁶_____ football, or any other sports? What do you like doing?

Write soon!

Ethan

4 ⭐⭐⭐ Write sentences about your likes, dislikes, fears and worries. Use adjectives from exercises 1–3.

I'm good at swimming and basketball, but I'm not
very good at running or football.
I'm a bit scared of ...

1 _____
2 _____
3 _____
4 _____
5 _____
6 _____

LANGUAGE FOCUS ◼ Modifiers • Present perfect: affirmative and negative

Modifiers

1 ⭐⭐ Order the words to make sentences.

not / swimming / fond / very / I'm / of
I'm not very fond of swimming.

1 really / Petra / is / driving / about / her / out / test / stressed

_____

2 in / Leo / interested / is / science / or / not / maths / very

_____

3 of / spiders / I'm / or / insects / not / fond / at / all

_____

4 we're / exams / our / summer / worried / very / about

_____

5 good / is / skiing / at / quite / Ugo

_____

6 India / scared / to / is / of / alone / Gina / travelling / a / bit

_____

Present perfect: affirmative and negative

2 ⭐ Complete the table with the words in the box.

> visited   has   he   eaten   haven't   I
> seen   hasn't

	Subject	*have*	Past participle and other words
✔	___I___ / you / we / they	have	played volleyball before.
	he / she / it	² _____	⁵ _____ three films this week.
✘	I / you / we / they	³ _____	⁶ _____ Paris.
	¹ _____ / she / it	⁴ _____	been on a helicopter.
			⁷ _____ sushi.

3 ⭐⭐ Write the past participle forms of the irregular verbs.

be _____been_____   6 buy _____
1 do _____   7 drive _____
2 eat _____   8 give _____
3 go _____   9 see _____
4 speak _____   10 take _____
5 win _____   11 write _____

4 ⭐⭐ Complete the sentences using the present perfect affirmative and negative form of the verbs.

You ___'ve bought___ (buy) a new CD, but you __haven't listened__ (not listen) to it.

1 I _____ (not visit) the Taj Mahal in India, but I _____ (study) its history at school.
2 My mum _____ (cook) snails, but I _____ (not eat) them.
3 He _____ (see) most of the Harry Potter films, but he _____ (not watch) the last one.
4 Karin and Jorg _____ (learn) some Japanese, but they _____ (not speak) to any Japanese people.
5 Adrian _____ (not touch) any big spiders, but he _____ (read) a lot of books about them.
6 We _____ (write) some new songs, but we _____ (not play) them at a concert.
7 I _____ (win) a skiing competition, but I _____ (not do) any snowboarding.

5 ⭐⭐⭐ Complete the text using the present perfect affirmative and negative of the verbs in the box.

> not win   play   d̶o̶   write
> not see   not finish

Fact file: Tennis player   Laura Robson

Laura Robson was born on 21st January 1994. She___'s done___ a lot of exciting things in her life! She ¹_____ tennis in tournaments all over the world.

Laura ²_____ college, so she takes all her books with her when she travels. A lot of journalists ³_____ newspaper articles about her, because she's a young British champion. Laura ⁴_____ a big tournament for adults yet, but everybody thinks she will one day!

Many people in Britain are excited about Laura. This is because they ⁵_____ a female British adult champion at Wimbledon for a long time.

VOCABULARY ■ Injuries

1 ★ Complete the words.

My little brother found a knife and now he's got a c__ut__ on his finger.

1 Be careful with that hot food from the microwave. Don't b_____ your hand.

2 Ivana has b_____ her arm again. She went to hospital to get it put in a plaster.

3 I fell off a rock in the mountains and now I've got this big black b_____ on my leg.

4 Those animals are dangerous because they can b_____ you.

5 He can't play rugby this weekend because he's got a really bad knee i_____.

6 Oh, no! I think I've s_____ my ankle.

2 ★★ Choose the correct answers.

She walked into a chair and now she's got a big blue and green _____ on her leg.

a burn **b bruise** c bite d cut

1 Oh, no! I've _____ my finger with the knife.
a cut b bitten c sprained d burnt

2 He's been on the beach for hours and he's _____ his face.
a bruised b burnt c injured d broken

3 That dog is very dangerous. It has _____ two people.
a broken b burnt c sprained d bitten

4 The best player in their team can't play because he's _____.
a broken b cut c injured d bitten

5 She's been in hospital for five weeks because she's _____ her leg.
a bitten b broken c bruised d sprained

6 Jean-Paul has got a nasty ankle _____.
a injure b bruised c injury d sprained

3 ★★ Complete the sentences with the words in the box.

> bitten sprained injured bruised ~~cut~~
> burn broken

The window was broken, so Joe was very careful. He didn't want to ___cut___ his hand.

1 He's _____ one of his teeth with a tennis racket. He needs to go to the dentist.

2 A lot of people were _____ in the train crash. They had terrible cuts and bruises.

3 She's fallen off her bike and she's _____ her arm. It's black and blue.

4 Wait! Don't eat the soup – it's very hot. You don't want to _____ your mouth.

5 A big insect has _____ my leg. It really hurts.

6 I fell and I _____ my ankle while I was playing rugby.

4 ★★★ Complete the postcard with the correct words.

Dear Susie,

I'm in Thailand on an adventure holiday. It's beautiful here, but I'm having a terrible time!

The weather is very hot and I've ___**burnt**___ my nose in the sun. There are also a lot of really big mosquitoes and I've got a ¹_____ on my arm.

I walked into a tree yesterday! I've ²_____ my face under my eye – it's all green and black! And this morning I broke a glass bottle and I've got a big ³_____ on my hand!

Last week one of the girls in our group fell while we were climbing a mountain. She ⁴_____ her arm and now she's gone back to the UK. I've never ⁵_____ my arm but I can imagine how much it hurts. I feel very sorry for her. I think I'm going to stay in my tent for the last week of the trip! I don't want another ⁶_____!

Love, Ashraf

LANGUAGE FOCUS ■ Present perfect: questions

8

1 ⭐ Choose the correct words to complete the table.

(Question word)	*have*	Subject	Past participle and other words
	Have	you	¹___ that film?
(Where) (What)	²___	Josh	been to Moscow?
	have	³___	gone?
	⁴___	Lisle	done with my money?

Answers
Yes, I ⁵___. / No, I haven't. Yes, he has. / No, he ⁶___. They've ⁷___ home. ⁸___ spent it all!

Have / has

1 seen / saw
2 Has / Have
3 he / they
4 has / have
5 has / have
6 have / hasn't
7 been / gone
8 She / She's

2 ⭐⭐ Write questions with *have* or *has*. Then match questions 1–6 with answers a–f.

1 you / hear / the new Jay-Z CD
   Have you heard the new Jay-Z CD? b

2 you / bruise / your finger
   _____

3 your brother / do / anything dangerous
   _____

4 we / finish / the lesson
   _____

5 your dad / sprain / his ankle
   _____

6 Michaela / ever / do / anything really frightening
   _____

a Yes, I have. My friend closed the door on it!
b Yes, I have. It's excellent.
c No, she hasn't. She prefers relaxing things.
d No, he hasn't. He's broken it.
e Yes, he has. He's climbed an active volcano!
f No, we haven't. There are five more minutes.

3 ⭐⭐ Write questions using *have / has* and *ever*.

she / see / a shark
Has she ever seen a shark?

1 you / break / your arm
   _____

2 they / sleep / outside in a storm
   _____

3 she / climb / a big mountain
   _____

4 you / meet / a pop star
   _____

5 he / play / rugby
   _____

6 we / watch / this programme before
   _____

4 ⭐⭐⭐ Write questions using *have / has* and *ever*. Then write short answers. Use the words in the boxes or your own ideas.

> your mum   dad   sister   brother
> best friend   teacher   parents

> see   break   burn   visit   climb
> be   play   meet

Has your mum ever been on a roller coaster?

Yes, she has.

1 _____
  _____

2 _____
  _____

3 _____
  _____

4 _____
  _____

5 _____
  _____

6 _____
  _____

Are you scared? ■ 67

The best roller coasters by Clara Brookes

I've been on twenty-five roller coasters in eight different countries. Why am I so enthusiastic about them? That's easy – they're fast and exciting! I've never found a ride which I'm frightened of.

I think the scariest roller coaster that I've tried is *Oblivion* at Alton Towers in the UK. You get into a special car and it climbs up to the top of the roller coaster. You stop for three seconds, and then you go down nearly sixty metres. You get a real feeling that you're going to die. I've taken about fifty photos of Oblivion.

My sister's been on it once, but she refused to go again – she was terrified of it. And my mum won't try the rides at all. She says they feel really unpleasant – I think she's a bit phobic about them. So I normally go on the roller coasters with my friends.

The roller coaster that I've visited the most is *Furius Baco* in Port Aventura, Spain. I've had three family holidays near Port Aventura, and we've been there many times. You travel from 0 to 135 kilometres an hour in 3.5 seconds, and your body feels really weird. You go upside down and look up at the sky – you can lose your money if you aren't careful.

The biggest and fastest roller coasters in the world are in the USA and Japan. I've asked my mum and dad about taking holidays there, but they think my love of roller coasters is ridiculous!

1 ★ Read the text. Tick ✔ the correct box.

Clara describes roller coasters in …

a ☐ Japan and Spain.
b ☐ Spain and the UK.
c ☐ the UK and Japan.

2 ★★ Read the text again. Choose the correct answers.

Clara has been on roller coasters in _____ countries.

a five (b eight) c twenty-five

1 At the top of *Oblivion* you _____ for a few seconds.
  a fall   b stop   c climb
2 Clara's sister thought *Oblivion* was very _____.
  a fast   b exciting   c scary
3 Clara's mum is _____ roller coasters.
  a good at   b keen on   c frightened of
4 On *Furius Baco* your _____ feels very strange.
  a hair   b neck   c body
5 Your speed on *Furius Baco* ___.
  a changes very fast
  b is always 135 kilometres an hour
  c is very weird
6 Clara's parents think that ___.
  a roller coasters are dangerous
  b Clara is a bit crazy to like roller coasters
  c the USA and Japan are ridiculous

3 ★★★ Answer the questions. Write complete sentences.

Why does Clara like roller coasters?

She likes them because they're fast and exciting.

1 Where is *Oblivion*?
_____

2 How many photos has Clara taken of *Oblivion*?
_____

3 How fast do you go on *Furius Baco*?
_____

4 How many times has Clara stayed near Port Aventura?
_____

5 Has Clara been to the largest roller coasters in the world?
_____

Build your vocabulary

4 ★★ Complete the sentences with words from the text in exercise 1.

I'm ¹p_____ about heights. I haven't been higher than the second floor of a building for about ten years. If I do, I get a very ²u_____ sensation that I'm going to fall. My legs don't work properly, and my head feels ³w_____, then I start to feel very sick. I know it sounds a bit ⁴r_____, but for me, the fear is very ⁵r_____. I feel stressed out about it, so I'm going to see a doctor.

8

Language point: *so* and *because*

1 ⭐ Complete the sentences with *so* or *because*.

I have a phobia of heights, __so__ I've never been mountain climbing.

1 I know Mike will win this match _____ he's really good at tennis.

2 Amy loves roller coasters, _____ she's enthusiastic about going to Alton Towers.

3 Isaac's skin burns easily, _____ he's not interested in a beach holiday.

4 We need to go to hospital _____ Nina's broken her ankle.

5 Ginette has spent all her money on CDs, _____ she can't afford to come out.

6 I'm stressed out _____ I've lost my mobile phone.

2 ⭐⭐ Order the words to make a short email.

going / Hi / it / Stefan / ? / how's

__Hi Stefan, how's it going?__

1 heard / you / have/ ? / Arturo / from

_____

2 hospital / he's / in / had / because / an / he's / accident

_____

3 fell / he / hit / head / off / and / his / his / bike

_____

4 they're / remember / so / he / anything / doing / some / couldn't / tests

_____

5 soon / write / news / I'll / with / more

_____

6 love / see / Petra / you

_____

⭕ TASK

3 ⭐⭐ Complete the email with the words in the box.

> so   heard   see   back   because   been
> so   ~~going~~   guess   interviewed

Delete Reply Reply All Forward New Mailboxes Get Mail   Q▾ From   Searc

Hi Emil,

How's it ___going___? I'm fine, but I've got some news. Have you ¹_____ from Peter this week? ²_____ what? He's ³_____ on TV! It rained a lot here last week and ⁴_____ the river got very high yesterday. Some people were in their cars in the water. They were very scared ⁵_____ they couldn't get out. Peter rescued a woman and her baby, ⁶_____ now he's a hero! Lots of journalists have ⁷_____ him and he's been on the TV news. Wow!

Write ⁸_____ soon, Emil, and tell me your news.

⁹_____ you,

Love Ingrid.

4 ⭐⭐⭐ Use the notes to write an email. Use the text in exercise 3 to help you.

- People: Charlie, writing to Claire, about Alice
- Situation: Alice / climb up a tree / fall off
- Problems: break leg / cut head
- Help: phone the police
- Now: in hospital until Sunday

VOCABULARY ● Feelings

1   Match sentence halves 1–6 with a–f.

1 Are you any good _____
2 I'm really fond _____
3 We're really bad _____
4 Jake is enthusiastic _____
5 Are you interested _____
6 Vinnie is scared _____

a in learning Japanese?
b about the trip. He can't wait to go.
c of spiders. He really hates them!
d at football. We lose every game!.
e of Indian food, but my family hate it.
f at chess? I can't play it at all!

> **I can explain how I feel about activities.**
>
> MY EVALUATION   ☐☐☐☐

READING ● Arachnophobia

2   Choose the correct words.

1 Was that a **real / really** accident on TV, or was it part of a film?
2 Katie is very **phobia / phobic** about small spaces.
3 Tim Burton's films are all quite **stranger / weird**.
4 Don't be **ridiculous / ridicule**! We can't stay here all night.
5 There's a very **pleasant / unpleasant** smell in the kitchen. I think the fish we bought last week has gone bad.

> **I can talk about fears and phobias.**
>
> MY EVALUATION   ☐☐☐☐

LANGUAGE FOCUS ● Present perfect: affirmative and negative

3   Complete the sentences with the present perfect form of the verbs in brackets.

1 I _____ (sprain) my ankle, but I _____ (not break) it.
2 My brother _____ (burn) his fingers. What should he do?
3 I _____ (have) problems with this bike, but I _____ (not fall) off it!
4 Carlo _____ (never / write) a letter to a celebrity.
5 Adrian and Imogen _____ (have) a car accident, but they're OK.
6 Oh no! My dog _____ (bite) my cousin!

> **I can talk about experiences.**
>
> MY EVALUATION   ☐☐☐☐

VOCABULARY ● Injuries

4   Complete the sentences with the correct past participle.

1 I've c_____ my finger with this knife.
2 Fran has b_____ her eye in a fight!
3 Carlo has s_____ his ankle, but he hasn't b_____ it.
4 Have you b_____ your skin in the sun?
5 How many players have i_____ themselves this season?
6 A mosquito has b_____ me all over my legs!

> **I can talk about injuries I've had.**
>
> MY EVALUATION   ☐☐☐☐

LANGUAGE FOCUS ■ Present perfect: questions

5 Write questions and short answers.

1 you / ever / break your leg (Yes)

_____

_____

2 Gina / see / the latest *Twilight* film (No)

_____

_____

3 Ben / try / riding a motorbike (No)

_____

_____

4 your parents / ever / travel / to Moscow (Yes)

_____

_____

5 you / eat / Greek food before (No)

_____

_____

6 Fran / do / her homework (Yes)

_____

_____

> **I can ask about people's experiences and react to their answers.**
>
> MY EVALUATION ☐☐☐☐

SPEAKING ■ Helping with problems

6 Match questions 1–5 with answers a–e.

1 What's wrong, Harry? _____
2 How did that happen? _____
3 Have you washed them? _____
4 Have you cut your arms? _____
5 Have you phoned your mum? _____

a No, I haven't. Can you get me some water?
b I've cut my hands and knees.
c Yes, I have. She's coming home from work now.
d No, I haven't. But maybe I've bruised them.
e I was playing tennis and I fell over.

> **I can help someone with an injury.**
>
> MY EVALUATION ☐☐☐☐

WRITING ■ Emails

7 Write two sentences to link the events, one with *so* and one with *because*.

I've broken my leg / we're going to hospital

I've <u>broken my leg, so we're going to hospital.</u>

We're <u>going to hospital because I've broken my leg.</u>

1 we're finishing the tennis match / one of the players is injured

We're _____

_____.

One _____

_____.

2 I was too tired / I fell when I was skiing

I fell _____

_____.

I was _____

_____.

3 I've written a letter of complaint / I thought the food was terrible

I've _____

_____.

I thought _____

_____

> **I can describe an accident.**
>
> MY EVALUATION ☐☐☐☐

be + subject pronouns

Affirmative		Negative	
Full form	**Short form**	**Full form**	**Short form**
I am You are	I'm You're	I am not You are not	I'm not You aren't
He / She / It is	He's / She's / It's	He is not She is not It is not	He isn't She isn't It isn't
We / You / They are	We're / You're / They're	We are not You are not They are not	We aren't You aren't They aren't

Subject pronouns cannot be left out of a sentence.
It's a good idea. ~~Is a good idea.~~
In spoken and informal written English, contracted forms are usually used.

Questions	Short answers	
	Affirmative	**Negative**
Am I happy? Are you happy?	Yes, I am. Yes, you are.	No, I'm not. No, you aren't.
Is he / she / it happy?	Yes, he / she / it is.	No, he / she / it isn't.
Are we / you/ they happy?	Yes, we / you/ they are.	No, we / you/ they aren't.

Contracted forms are used in negative (but not affirmative) short answers.
Is he French? Yes, he is. ~~Yes, he's.~~
Interrogative pronouns go before the verb *be*.
Where are you from? ~~You are from where?~~

Use
The verb *be* is used to talk about personal information.
I'm 13 years old. My name is Carmen. Are you from the UK?

Possessive *'s*

The possessive *'s* is used to show that something belongs to somebody and also for relationships.
This is Sophie's pen.   **I'm Ben's brother.**
For singular nouns add *'s* to the noun.
My cousin's house. (one cousin)
For plural nouns add *'*.
My cousins' house. (two or more cousins)
For irregular plural nouns add *'s*.
the children's mother
When there is more than one noun, add *'s* to the last noun only.
Emma and Dan's father

have got

Affirmative	Negative
I've got a new teacher. You've got a new teacher.	I haven't got a new teacher. You haven't got a new teacher.
He's / She's / It's got a new teacher.	He / She / It hasn't got a new teacher.
We've / You've / They've got a new teacher	We / You / They haven't got a new teacher.

In spoken and informal written English contracted forms are usually used.

Questions	Short answers	
	Affirmative	**Negative**
Have I got homework?	Yes, I have.	No, I haven't.
Have you got homework?	Yes, you have.	No, you haven't.
Has he / she / it got homework?	Yes, he / she / it has.	No, he / she / it hasn't.
Have we / you / they got homework?	Yes, we / you / they have.	No, we / you / they haven't.

Short answers are made with *have* without *got*.
Yes, I have.   NOT ~~Yes, I have got.~~

Use
Have got is used to talk about possession, family relationships and things that you need to do.
I've got an English book.
He's got a sister.
We've got a French exam.

there is, there are

	Affirmative	Negative	Questions
Singular	There's a science laboratory.	There isn't a music room.	Is there an exam on Wednesday?
Plural	There are three new students.	There aren't any new teachers.	Are there any books on the table?

In spoken and informal written English contracted forms are usually used. However, there is no contracted form of *there are*.
There are books in my bag.
NOT ~~There're books in my bag.~~

Uses
there is / there are is used to describe the existence or absence of someone or something.

be + subject pronouns

1 Complete the sentences with the correct form of *be*.

Claudia __is__ my aunt.

1 We _____ football fans. We like tennis.
2 _____ your brother interested in history?
3 I _____ from Gdansk.
4 It _____ five o'clock. It's six o'clock.
5 _____ your cousins good at English?
6 You _____ in my class at school. You sit near me.
7 What _____ your brothers' names?
8 _____ you happy today?

2 Choose the correct words.

We've got a new DVD. (It)/ He's very good.

1 This is my friend Antonio. **He / She**'s from Argentina.
2 Ruby and James aren't in class today. **We / They**'re at home.
3 Pierre and I are French and **you / we**'re from Marseilles.
4 Are you interested in science? No, **I / they** like maths.
5 My friends are Italian. **You / They** live in Rome.
6 Clare isn't British. **She / He**'s American.
7 Am I late? Yes, **you / I** are.
8 My dad is tall. **He / She**'s 1m 90.

Possessive *'s*

3 Write sentences with the possessive *'s*.

Is this your (mother / book)?
Is this your mother's book?

1 Are you (Rory and Paul / cousin)?
_____
2 We like (David / computer).
_____
3 My (grandparents / names) are Alan and Ann.
_____
4 The (twins / birthday) is on Tuesday.
_____
5 My (sister / room) is blue.
_____
6 This is the (children / school).
_____

have got

4 Write affirmative or negative sentences with *have got*.

she / a brother and a sister
She's got a brother and a sister.

1 we / maths today
_____
2 you / not / any history homework
_____
3 I / not / black hair
_____
4 he / not / a strict teacher
_____
5 they / four children
_____
6 my school / not / a swimming pool
_____

5 Write questions and short answers with *have got*.

they / a nice teacher ✓
Have they got a nice teacher?
Yes, they have.

1 she / an English dictionary ✗
_____
_____
2 we / a French exam ✗
_____
_____
3 you / a geography lesson now ✓
_____
_____

there is, there are

6 Complete the sentences with the affirmative and negative forms of *there is* and *there are*.

__There are__ two exams on Tuesday.

1 _____ a big science laboratory in our school.
2 We haven't got a maths lesson today because _____ a teacher.
3 No, _____ any history books on my table.
4 _____ any new students in your class?
5 _____ a music room in your school?
6 No, _____ a school uniform at my school.

Present simple: affirmative and negative

Affirmative	Negative
I play tennis. You play tennis.	I don't play tennis. You don't play tennis.
He plays tennis. She plays tennis. It plays tennis.	He doesn't play tennis. She doesn't play tennis. It doesn't play tennis.
We play tennis. You play tennis. They play tennis.	We don't play tennis. You don't play tennis. They don't play tennis.

Present simple: he / she / it + verb + s – spelling rules

Most verbs:	add -s	needs wears changes wants
Verbs ending in a consonant + -y:	drop the -y and add -ies	carries studies tidies marries
Verbs ending in -o, -ch, -sh, -x and -ss:	add -es.	goes watches washes fixes misses

In spoken and informal written English contracted forms *don't* and *doesn't* are usually used.

Use
We use the present simple:
to describe things which happen regularly or all the time.
I ride my bike to school every day.
It's cold in winter.
to describe permanent situations.
We live in a nice town.
to give opinions.
I don't like reggae.

Adverbs of frequency

100% ⟶ 0%
always usually often sometimes
occasionally not often hardly ever never

Uses
Adverbs of frequency describe how often something happens.
He is **often** late for school.
Have you **usually** got your ID card with you?
They don't **often** go to the cinema.
I've **always** got my mobile phone with me.

Position of adverbs of frequency

Affirmative	be	after the verb
	have got	between *have* and *got*
	other verbs	before the verb
Negative	be	after the verb
	have got	between *have* and *got*
	other verbs	between *don't / doesn't* and the verb
Questions	be	after the subject
	have got	between the subject and *got*
	other verbs	before the verb

Present simple: questions

Questions	Short answers	
	Affirmative	Negative
Do I play football?	Yes, I do.	No, I don't.
Do you play football?	Yes, you do.	No, you don't.
Does he play football?	Yes, he does.	No, he doesn't.
Does she play football?	Yes, she does.	No, she doesn't.
Does it play football?	Yes, it does.	No, it doesn't.
Do we play football?	Yes, we do.	No, we don't.
Do you play football?	Yes, you do.	No, you don't.
Do they play football?	Yes, they do.	No, they don't.

Interrogative pronouns (*Who, What, When*, etc.) go before *do / does*.
What do you like?

Present simple: affirmative and negative

1 Write the third person singular (*he / she / it*) form of the verbs.

carry   _carries_
1 watch   _____
2 use   _____
3 study   _____
4 finish   _____
5 need   _____
6 wear   _____
7 go   _____
8 have   _____

2 Complete the sentences with the correct form of the verbs in the box.

> not wear   carry   not play   ~~finish~~
> not watch   change   go

My dad ___*finishes*___ work at six o'clock.
1 Julie _____ any make-up.
2 We _____ to school by bus.
3 My sister _____ football.
4 Leo always _____ his MP3 player in his bag.
5 Mum usually _____ her clothes after work.
6 I _____ TV before school.

Adverbs of frequency

3 Put the adverbs of frequency in the correct order.

> not often   ~~hardly ever~~   occasionally
> often   sometimes   usually

never   _hardly ever_
           1 _____
           2 _____
           3 _____
           4 _____
           5 _____
always

4 Choose the correct words.

I **'ve sometimes got** / 've got sometimes my laptop with me.
1 She**'s hardly ever** / hardly is ever late for school.
2 We **go sometimes** / **sometimes go** shopping on Saturdays.
3 They **often are** / **'re often** tired in the evenings.
4 It**'s usually** / **usually is** very hot here in summer.
5 You **never have got** / **'ve never got** any money with you.
6 Liam **doesn't often play** / **plays not often** football.

Present simple: questions

5 Rewrite the sentences as questions.

He goes to school by car.
Does he go to school by car?
1 I need my ID card for school.
_____
2 She carries a lot of things in her bag.
_____
3 You watch too much TV.
_____
4 They use the laptop for their homework.
_____
5 We finish school at three o'clock today.
_____
6 Joe plays basketball.
_____

6 Put the words in the correct order.

listen to / music/ what / you / do
What music do you listen to?
1 your / meet / where / you / do / friends
_____
2 books / what / you / read / do
_____
3 like / shopping / do / why / you
_____
4 watch / when / TV / you / do
_____
5 do / who / the / with / go / cinema / to / you
_____

Present continuous: affirmative and negative

Affirmative	Negative
I'm chatting.	I'm not chatting.
You're chatting.	You aren't chatting.
He's chatting.	He isn't chatting.
She's chatting.	She isn't chatting.
It's chatting.	It isn't chatting.
We're chatting.	We aren't chatting.
You're chatting.	You aren't chatting.
They're chatting.	They aren't chatting.

The affirmative form of the present continuous is made with the verb *be* and the *-ing* form of the verb.

The negative form is made with the verb *be* + *not* and the *-ing* form of the verb.

Note that in spoken and informal written English contracted forms are used.

Present continuous: questions

Questions	Short answers	
	Affirmative	Negative
Am I studying?	Yes, I am.	No, I'm not.
Are you studying?	Yes, you are.	No, you aren't.
Is he studying?	Yes, he is.	No, he isn't.
Is she studying?	Yes, she is.	No, she isn't.
Is it studying?	Yes, it is.	No, it isn't.
Are we studying?	Yes, we are.	No, we aren't.
Are you studying?	Yes, you are.	No, you aren't.
Are they studying?	Yes, they are.	No, they aren't.

The question form is made by inverting the verb *be* and the *-ing* form.

Short answers are made with the verb *be* only, without the *-ing* form of the main verb.

Don't use contractions in positive short answers.

Yes, I am.   NOT ~~Yes, I'm.~~

Yes, she is.   NOT ~~Yes, she's.~~

Yes, we are.   NOT ~~Yes, we're.~~

Question words go before the verb *be*.

What are you making for lunch?

Why is he cleaning the floor now?

Present simple and present continuous

Use

The present continuous is used to talk about an action in progress. Time expressions like *now* or *at the moment* are often used with the present continuous.

Where's Karl now? He's making his bed.

They're doing their homework at the moment.

The present simple is used to talk about routine or repeated action. We often use adverbs of frequency like *always, often* or *usually* with the present simple.

He has a shower every morning.

We usually do the washing-up after dinner.

Note that there are some verbs (stative verbs) which are not normally used in the continuous form, because they describe states which remain true, not actions in progress. These include:

understand, know, think, like, love, hate and *want*.

I like your new sofa.

NOT ~~I'm liking your new sofa.~~

Do you want a coffee?

NOT ~~Are you wanting a coffee?~~

Present continuous: affirmative and negative

1 Write the *-ing* form of these verbs.

carry   <u>carrying</u>

1 study   _____
2 make   _____
3 tidy   _____
4 run   _____
5 clean   _____
6 write   _____
7 swim   _____
8 have   _____

2 Complete the sentences with the present continuous form of the verbs in brackets.

My brother _____ <u>is tidying</u> _____ (tidy) his bedroom.

1 You _____ (not use) the new microwave.
2 Paul _____ (sit) on a chair next to the window.
3 Diego and Jorge _____ (not make) dinner now.
4 We _____ (do) the washing-up now.
5 I _____ (eat) lunch in a café near the school.
6 Rita _____ (not clean) the floor at the moment.

3 Rewrite the sentences using the negative form.

We're reading a magazine.
<u>We aren't reading a magazine.</u>

1 They're doing the washing-up.
   _____

2 He's spending a lot of money at the shops.
   _____

3 I'm tidying the kitchen.
   _____

4 You're listening to me.
   _____

5 Marta is having a shower.
   _____

6 We're watching TV.
   _____

Present continuous: questions

4 Write questions using the present continuous. Then complete the short answers.

your brother / sit / under the tree
<u>Is your brother sitting under the tree?</u>

Yes, <u>he is</u>_____.

1 we / write / in German
   _____
   No, _____.
2 they / buy / a new bookcase
   _____
   Yes, _____.
3 you / use / the washing machine
   _____
   Yes, _____.
4 she / play / near the house
   _____
   No, _____.

Present simple and present continuous

5 Choose the correct words.

Where's Daniela? She ⟨**'s making**⟩ / **makes** breakfast in the kitchen.

1 My teacher **is going** / **goes** to Italy every summer.
2 I'm very busy at the moment. I **'m doing** / **do** the ironing.
3 Come in and sit down. We **'re watching** / **watch** a great film.
4 They **'re cleaning** / **clean** the house on Saturday mornings.
5 Paul **isn't playing** / **doesn't play** football every day.

6 Complete the letter with the correct form of the verbs in brackets.

Hi, Clara! How are you? I ____ **'m having** ____ (have) a fantastic holiday in France and we
¹_____ (stay) in a nice new hotel. It's really hot today and I ²_____ (sit) under a big tree at the moment!
We ³_____ (visit) the same village every year and we usually ⁴_____ (go) to the same restaurant every night! My dad always ⁵_____ (have) traditional French food for dinner, but I ⁶_____ (not like) it – I prefer pizza!
What ⁷_____ (you / do) now?
See you soon,
Isabel

was, were

Was and *were* are the past simple forms of the verb *to be*.

Affirmative	Negative
I was nervous.	I wasn't nervous.
You were nervous.	You weren't nervous.
He / She / It was nervous.	He / She / It wasn't nervous.
We / You / They were nervous.	We / You / They weren't nervous.

The negative forms of *was* and *were* are *was not* and *were not*. However, in spoken and informal written English, we use the contracted forms .
James wasn't at home. NOT ~~James no was at home.~~

Questions	Short answers
Was I nervous?	Yes, I was. / No, I wasn't.
Were you nervous?	Yes, you were. / No, you weren't.
Was he / she / it nervous?	Yes, he / she / it / was. No, he / she / it wasn't.
Were / we / you / they nervous?	Yes, we / you /they were. / No, they / we / you / weren't.

Question words go before *was / were*.
Where were you? NOT ~~Where you were?~~

there was, there were

There was and *there were* are the past simple forms of *there is* and *there are*.
There was some food on the table.
There were twenty students in the class.
The negative forms are *there wasn't* and *there weren't*.
There wasn't any money. There weren't any oranges.
Make the question form by inverting *was / were* and *there*.
Was there anything to eat?
NOT ~~There was anything to eat?~~
Were there a lot of people?
NOT ~~There were a lot of people?~~
It is common to use the contracted form in negative short answers.
Yes, there was. / No, there weren't.

Use
Use *there was* and *there were* to describe what existed in the past.
There were two houses here. There was a big museum.

Past simple

Affirmative	
Regular	**Irregular**
I / You started school.	I / You left school.
He / She / It started school.	He / She / It left school.
We / You / They started school.	We / You / They left school.

Make the affirmative form of past simple regular verbs by adding *-d* or *-ed* to the base form.
He closed the door.
Irregular verbs each have a different past simple form. (See page 104.)
Tom ate all of the sandwiches.
Remember: Each verb in the past simple has only one form.
Our parents got married in 1982. I got married in 2009, and my sister got married two years later.

Negative	
Regular	**Irregular**
I / You didn't start school.	I / You didn't leave school.
He / She / It didn't start school.	He / She / It didn't leave school.
We / You / They didn't start school.	We / You / They didn't leave school.

Questions			
	Regular	**Irregular**	**Answers**
	Did I / you start school?	Did I / you leave school?	I / you started / left school.
When	did he / she / it start school?	did he / she / it leave school?	He / She / It started / left school in ...
Why	did we / you / they start school?	did we / you / they leave school?	We / you / they started / left school because ...

The question form is made with the auxiliary verb *did* plus the base form.
Where did they get married? NOT ~~Where they got married?~~

Use
Use the past simple to describe events which happened at a specific time in the past.
I bought my first house in 2007.

Time expressions and *ago*

Use *ago* with periods of time such as *two years*, to say how far in the past an event happened.
I last played football two months ago. (= two months before now)

Past simple: affirmative, negative and questions

1 Complete the text with the past simple form of the verbs.

> not have   become   leave   not move
> not buy   ~~get~~   graduate   have

My parents _____**got**_____ married in 1985.
They ¹_____ a house because they
²_____ a lot of money. A year later
my dad ³_____ from university. My
parents ⁴_____ two children, me
and my sister, Hana. Three years ago Hana
⁵_____ school and ⁶_____
a nurse. But she ⁷_____ into her own
flat. She's happy at home!

2 Complete the questions with the past simple form of the verbs. Then complete the short answers.

_____**Did**_____ he _____**spend**_____ (spend) a lot of
money today?
Yes, _____**he did**_____.

1 _____ they _____ (get up) at
six o'clock?
Yes, _____.

2 _____ you _____ (enjoy) the
party?
No, _____.

3 _____ she _____ (have) a sister?
Yes, _____.

4 _____ I _____ (send) you an
email?
No, _____.

3 Order the words to make questions.

graduate / when / you / did
When did you graduate?

1 buy / she / the house / did / why
_____

2 have / you / how many / did / children
_____

3 did / what / he / at school / do / ?
_____

4 the / competition / did / they / how / win
_____

5 that / coat / did / you / where / buy
_____

was, were

4 Complete the sentences and questions with *was, were, wasn't* and *weren't*.

I _____**wasn't**_____ in the kitchen. I was in my bedroom.

1 The concert _____ fun. It wasn't boring.

2 The children weren't friendly. They _____ horrible.

3 _____ she your teacher? No, she
_____.

4 My sister _____ at the party. She was at work.

5 We were at the same school, but we
_____ in the same class.

6 Where _____ you yesterday?
We _____ at home.

there was, there were

5 Complete the sentences with *there was, there wasn't, there were* and *there weren't*.

_____**There were**_____ a lot of people at my party. ✓

1 _____ any music in the CD player. ✗

2 _____ a lot of money on the table. ✓

3 _____ any good programmes on TV. ✗

4 _____ some pasta for dinner. ✓

5 _____ any chips. ✗

6 _____ two books in my bag. ✓

Time expressions and *ago*

6 Order the words to make sentences. Use the past simple form of the verb.

a new house / I / two weeks / buy / ago
I bought a new house two weeks ago.

1 Jack / ago / home / three / leave / months
_____

2 we / a scary film / ago / see / two days
_____

3 get / ago / married / sister / a year / my
_____

4 two / I / weeks / graduate / ago
_____

5 a month / we / school / ago / start
_____

6 finish / ago / the / ten / film / minutes
_____

Past continuous: affirmative and negative

Affirmative	Negative
I was running.	I wasn't running.
You were running.	You weren't running.
He was running.	He wasn't running.
She was running.	She wasn't running.
It was running.	It wasn't running.
We were running.	We weren't running.
You were running.	You weren't running.
They were running.	They weren't running.

The affirmative form of the past continuous is made with *was* or *were* after the subject. This is followed by the *-ing* form of the main verb.
The negative form is made by putting *not* between *was* or *were* and the *-ing* form of the main verb.
Note that in spoken and informal written English, the contracted forms *wasn't* and *weren't* are used.

Past continuous: questions

Questions	Short answers	
	Affirmative	Negative
Was I walking?	Yes, I was.	No, I wasn't.
Were you walking?	Yes, you were.	No, you weren't.
Was he walking?	Yes, he was.	No, he wasn't.
Was she walking?	Yes, she was.	No, she wasn't.
Was it walking?	Yes, it was.	No, it wasn't.
Were we walking?	Yes, we were.	No, we weren't.
Were you walking?	Yes, you were.	No, you weren't.
Were they walking?	Yes, they were.	No, they weren't.

The question form is made by putting *was* or *were* before the subject at the beginning of the question.
Short answers are made with the subject and *was* or *were*, without the *-ing* form of the main verb.
Question words go before *was* or *were*.
What were you doing in the mountains?
Why was she climbing up the tree?

Use

Use the past continuous to talk about actions in progress at a point in the past. We often use expressions to show the point of time, such as *at* (+ time) or *when* (+ a past simple action).
It was raining at ten o'clock yesterday.
What were they doing on Saturday afternoon?
You weren't listening to the teacher when she asked the question.

Past simple and past continuous

Use

We often use the past continuous to describe an action in progress which was interrupted.
She was cycling down the mountain when she fell off her bike.

We use the past continuous for the longer action in progress (*was cycling*). We use the past simple (*fell off*) for the shorter action which interrupts the longer one.

We often use *when* before the past simple and *while* before the past continuous.
They were travelling across Antarctica when they saw penguins.
They saw penguins while they were travelling across Antarctica.

UNIT 4 ● LANGUAGE FOCUS PRACTICE

Past continuous: affirmative and negative

1 Complete the sentences with *was, wasn't, were* or *weren't*.

We __were__ listening to music on our MP3 player. ✓

1 It _____ raining again this afternoon. ✓
2 She _____ talking to Laura on the phone. ✗
3 You _____ walking to school. ✗
4 He _____ driving across Europe on holiday. ✓
5 They _____ sailing around the Mediterranean. ✗

2 Complete the sentences with the past continuous form of these verbs.

> cycle   not talk   have   not rain
> not study   ~~watch~~   not wear

Yesterday afternoon ...

Dave __was watching__ a film on TV.

1 Ana and Carmen _____ through the park on their bikes.
2 Jake _____ a coat.
3 I _____ lunch with my parents.
4 It _____ – it was sunny.
5 We _____ because it was a holiday!
6 I _____ to Gina, because she was asleep.

Past continuous: questions

3 Write questions using the past continuous.

what / you / do / yesterday
__What were you doing yesterday?__

1 why / your sister / carry / a big bag
_____
2 Sam / play / in the basketball match
_____
3 your friends / walk / near the river
_____
4 what / they / talk about
_____
5 where / the train / go
_____
6 who / you / talk to
_____

Past simple and past continuous

4 Choose the correct words.

When Emma (arrived)/ was arriving at the airport, her mother waited /(was waiting) for her.

1 It **started** / **was starting** to snow while we **watched** / **were watching** the match.
2 The tourists **drove** / **were driving** across the desert when they **had** / **were having** an accident.
3 I **saw** / **was seeing** a famous actor near the theatre. He **wore** / **was wearing** sunglasses.
4 Tomiko **met** / **was meeting** a Japanese boy while she **travelled** / **was travelling** across Australia.
5 We **were skiing** / **skied** down the mountain when Tom **was falling** / **fell** over.
6 You **didn't wear** / **weren't wearing** a cycle helmet when you **arrived** / **were arriving** home.
7 Rob and Kate **arrived** / **were arriving** while we **watched** / **were watching** TV.

5 Complete the email using the past simple or past continuous form of the verbs.

● ● ●

🚫 ↩ ↩ ➡ 📝 📇 ✉   Q▾ From

Delete Reply Reply All Forward New Mailboxes Get Mail   Search Mailbox

Hi, Amy!

Guess what! I __was cycling__ (cycle) home from school today when suddenly a little boy [1]_____ (walk) in front of me. He [2]_____ (not look) and his mum and dad [3]_____ (chat). I [4]_____ (go) very fast on my bike but I [5]_____ (stop) before I hit the boy. His mum was very nice and she [6]_____ (say) sorry to me.

See you tomorrow,

Noah

Ability: *can* and *could*

Affirmative	Negative
I / You can dance.	I / You can't dance.
He / She / It can dance.	He / She / It can't dance.
We / You / They can dance.	We / You / They can't dance.

Questions	Short answers
Can Maria dance?	Yes, she can. / No, she can't.

Affirmative	Negative
I / You could sing.	I / You couldn't sing.
He / She / It could sing.	He / She / It couldn't sing.
We / You / They could sing.	We / You / They couldn't sing.

Questions	Short answers
Could they sing?	Yes, they could. / No, they couldn't.

Can and *could* each have only one form. They do not change with different subjects.

I can play tennis.   He can play tennis.
NOT *He cans play tennis.* OR *He can plays tennis.*
We use *can* / *could* + the base form of the main verb.
You can speak Italian.   NOT *You can to speak Italian.*
She could play the piano.
NOT *She could to play the piano.*
The negative forms of *can* and *could* are *can not* and *could not*. However, in spoken and informal written English, the contracted forms *can't* and *couldn't* are usually used.
Francis can't dive.   NOT *Francis doesn't can dive.*
We couldn't go out.   NOT *We didn't can go out.*
As with *can* and *could*, the main verb takes the base form.
We can't cook.   NOT *We can't to cook.*
They couldn't play tennis.
NOT *They couldn't to play tennis.*

Use

Can and *could* describe the ability to do something.
I can swim.
She could read when she was three.
Can describes the ability to do something in the present.
Now I can dance flamenco.
Could describes the ability to do something in the past.
He could sing in Russian when he was little.

Questions with *How ... ?*

To make questions with *how*, use *how* + *often*, *much* / *many* or an adjective.
How often do they go swimming?
How much money do you spend?
How long is her hair?

Use

We use questions with *how* when we want to know the frequency, measurement or quantity of something.
How much water do you drink?
How many brothers and sisters have you got?
How far can you run?
How strict are your teachers?
We only use *often* with *how* to ask about frequency.
How often do you go shopping?
NOT *How usually / sometimes / rarely do you go shopping?*

Comparative and superlative adjectives

Adjective	Comparative	Superlative
Most one-syllable adjectives	add -er fast – faster	add -est wild – wildest
One syllable with one vowel and ending in one consonant	double consonant and add -er big – bigger	double consonant and add -est fat – fattest
One syllable ending in -e	add -r rare – rarer	add -st large – largest
Adjectives of two or more syllables ending in -y	remove -y and add -ier heavy – heavier	remove -y and add -iest happy – happiest
All other adjectives of two or more syllables	put *more* before adjective artistic – more artistic	put *most* before adjective practical – most practical
Irregular	good – better bad – worse	good – best bad – worst

Use

Use comparative adjectives to compare two objects or people, or two groups of objects or people.
Jenny is taller than Hugh.
Use superlative adjectives to say that a person, object or group of people or objects, has the greatest amount of a characteristic, compared to everything else in that group.
Blue whales are the biggest animals in the world.

Ability: *can* and *could*

1 Complete the sentences with *can, can't, could, couldn't* and the correct form of the verb.

When I was three months old I ___couldn't walk___ (walk).

1 Matthew is very intelligent. He
_____ (speak) five languages.
2 Rob and I watched a Japanese film last night, but we _____ (understand) it.
3 My grandma was very good at music. She
_____ (play) the piano and sing.
4 I can use a computer, but I _____
(program) one.
5 Adam and Paul are brilliant cooks – they
_____ (make) really tasty food.

2 Choose the correct words.

Henry **didn't could** / (couldn't) speak French two years ago.

1 The girls can **play** / **to play** chess.
2 I **can** / **could** ride a horse when I was three.
3 We **don't can** / **can't** swim across the lake.
4 Alicia **can** / **cans** compose music.
5 My brother couldn't **to ski** / **ski** on holiday last year.

Questions with *How ... ?*

3 Read the answers. Then complete the questions with *how* and the words in the box.

much   far   many   friendly   strict
often   ~~tall~~

___How tall___ are you?
I'm one metre seventy.

1 _____ apples do you eat every day? One or two.
2 _____ does he play basketball? Three times a week.
3 _____ is your teacher? Not very. He's usually friendly.
4 _____ can you run? About a kilometre.
5 _____ pasta is there? There's enough for two people.
6 _____ is your cat? Not very. Sometimes, he bites people!

Comparative and superlative adjectives

4 Complete the table with the comparative and superlative forms of the adjectives.

Adjective	Comparative	Superlative
big	_bigger_	_the biggest_
bad		
far		
heavy		
intelligent		
large		
light		
peaceful		
unhappy		

5 Complete the text with the comparative or superlative forms of the adjectives.

I've got three really good friends – Cara, Suzy and Megan. Cara is _____older_____ (old) than us – she's fifteen and we're all fourteen. Megan is the [1] _____ (young) – she had her fourteenth birthday last week. Suzy is the [2] _____ (tall) – she's one metre eighty-five! I'm one metre sixty, but Cara is [3] _____ (short) than me – she's only one metre fifty.

The [4] _____ (intelligent) person is definitely Cara . But Megan is [5] _____ (artistic) than Cara. She can paint really good pictures. Suzy is the [6] _____ (funny) person I know. I'm [7] _____ (quiet) than all of them, but we always have fun!

6 Write sentences with comparative and superlative adjectives.

my dad / artistic / person in our family
My dad is the most artistic person in our family.

1 cats / slow / tigers
_____

2 elephants / rare / dogs
_____

3 humans / intelligent / animals in the world
_____

4 I / practical / my sister
_____

5 you / good / singer in the class
_____

will and won't

Affirmative	Negative
I'll buy a house.	I won't buy a house.
You'll buy a house.	You won't buy a house.
He'll buy a house.	He won't buy a house.
She'll buy a house.	She won't buy a house.
It'll buy a house.	It won't buy a house.
We'll buy a house.	We won't buy a house.
You'll buy a house.	You won't buy a house.
They'll buy a house.	They won't buy a house.

The affirmative form is made with *will* + the base form.

Jake will be fifteen next month.

Note that in spoken and informal written English the contracted form *'ll* is usually used after a subject pronoun.

The negative form is made with *won't* (*will not*) + the base form.

Lenka won't be late. NOT ~~Lenka won't to be late.~~

Note that in spoken and informal written English contracted forms are used.

I'll become a doctor one day. **They won't be famous.**

Questions	Short answers	
	Affirmative	Negative
Will I understand?	Yes, I will.	No, I won't.
Will you understand?	Yes, you will.	No, you won't.
Will he understand?	Yes, he will.	No, he won't.
Will she understand?	Yes, she will.	No, she won't.
Will it understand?	Yes, it will.	No, it won't.
Will we understand?	Yes, we will.	No, we won't.
Will you understand?	Yes, you will.	No, you won't.
Will they understand?	Yes, they will.	No, they won't.

Don't use the contracted form in positive short answers.

Will Harry be there? **Yes, he will.** NOT ~~Yes, he'll.~~

Question words go at the beginning of the question, before *will*.

What will people eat in the future?

NOT ~~People will eat what in the future?~~

Use

Use *will* and *won't* to make predictions about the future.

She'll win the tennis match tomorrow.

We won't move to a different house.

First conditional

Action	Result
If I walk slowly,	I'll arrive late.
If you walk slowly,	you'll arrive late.
If he runs quickly,	he'll arrive at two o'clock.
If she runs quickly,	she'll arrive at two o'clock.
If it runs quickly,	it'll arrive at two o'clock.
If we go by car,	we'll arrive early.
If you go by car,	you'll arrive early.
If they go by car,	they'll arrive early.

The first conditional is formed with *if* + present simple clause, + *will* clause.

If you come to town, I'll meet you.

Conditional sentences can start with the action:

If you learn English, you'll understand American films.

or with the result:

You'll understand American films if you learn English.

We can use the negative form in the action, the result, or both parts of the sentence.

If I don't leave now, I won't meet James at the station.

Make first conditional questions with *will* in front of the subject in the result clause.

Will you help me if I give you some money?

NOT ~~Do you help me …?~~

If I give you some money, will you help me?

NOT ~~If I will give you …~~

Use

Use the first conditional to predict the result of an action.

We use it to talk about things that we think might happen in the future, and things we think are possible.

Expressing probability

Use the adverbs *probably* or *definitely* to say how likely you think an event is to happen.

She'll definitely win the game.

I disagree! I think she'll probably lose.

In the affirmative form, adverbs go after the verb *will*. In the negative form, adverbs go before the verb *won't*.

Vinnie will definitely be in the team.

NOT ~~Vinnie definitely will be in the team.~~

Renée probably won't play today.

NOT ~~Renée won't probably play today.~~

UNIT 6 ■ LANGUAGE FOCUS PRACTICE

will and *won't*

1 Complete the sentences with *will* or *won't* and the verbs in the box.

> be   not give   win   leave   ~~work~~   not use

I think you ____'ll work____ in a TV studio.

1 He _____ you a birthday present because he isn't very generous.
2 When _____ you _____ home?
3 They _____ that new computer because it's very complicated.
4 I'm sure she _____ a pop star when she's older.
5 _____ our team _____ the match tomorrow?

2 Complete the sentences with *will* and *won't* and the verb in brackets.

You ___won't lose___ (not lose) the match tomorrow. You _____'ll win_____ (win)!

1 Carmen _____ (love) this film. She _____ (not think) it's boring.
2 In 2040 children _____ (learn) Mandarin. They _____ (not study) English.
3 I think I _____ (be) a teacher. I _____ (not become) a doctor.
4 People _____ (not go) to a different planet in the next millennium. They _____ (live) here.
5 I'm pretty sure that we _____ (visit) New York next year. But we _____ (not stay) in a hotel.

3 Order the words to make questions.

it / tomorrow / rain / will

__Will it rain tomorrow?__

1 go / to / when / university / you / will
_____
2 one / day / we / be / will / famous
_____
3 they / will / on / where / holiday / go
_____
4 what / do / she / will / tonight
_____
5 the / will / match / win / they
_____
6 at / will / party / the / be / Rosie
_____

First conditional

4 Choose the correct words.

If they (don't come)/ won't come now, we are /('ll be) late again.

1 He **won't read** / **don't read** his poem in class tomorrow if he **feels** / **'ll feel** shy.
2 If it **will rain** / **rains** on Monday, we **go** / **'ll go** to the café.
3 **Will you** / **Do you** answer this survey if I **help** / **'ll help** you with the questions?
4 If you**'re** / **'ll be** very positive, you **do** / **'ll do** well at school.
5 I **give** / **'ll give** you that new book if you **tidy** / **'ll tidy** your bedroom.

5 Complete the sentences with the correct form of the verbs in brackets.

If I ___buy___ (buy) that magazine, I ___'ll read___ (read) the horoscopes first.

1 They _____ (not go) on holiday if they _____ (get) a new car.
2 If he _____ (become) a professional footballer, will he _____ (move) to a different town?
3 She _____ (not study) maths if she _____ (go) to university.
4 If you _____ (find) some money, _____ (be) very happy!
5 If we _____ (go) to the party, _____ (see) Aisha and Chris.

Expressing probability

6 Complete the sentences with *will* or *won't* and *probably* or *definitely* in the correct order, to match the probabilities in brackets.

Meena __definitely won't__ study Chemistry. She hates it! (0%)

I __'ll probably__ be late tonight. My bus isn't here. (60%)

1 I _____ come out, because I don't feel very well. (20%)
2 My mum _____ be angry if I'm late! (100%)
3 We _____ go shopping on Saturday. I'm not sure. (70%)
4 We _____ fly so much in the future. It's so bad for the environment. (0%)

Imperatives

Affirmative imperatives use the base form of the verb.

Do your homework. NOT ~~To do your homework.~~

The form is the same, if the instruction is for one person or more than one.

Kate, do the washing up! **Kate and Alex, tidy your rooms!**

Negative imperatives use *don't* + the base form.

Don't forget to phone me!

NOT ~~No forget to phone me!~~

This includes the verb *be*, but this is the only time we use *don't* before the verb *be*.

Don't be late!

In imperative sentences we don't use the subject pronoun.

Come here! NOT ~~You come here!~~

Don't eat in here. NOT ~~You don't eat in here.~~

Use

We use imperatives to give an instruction or order to do or not to do something, and to give advice.

Talk to the manager. Don't listen to him.

be going to

Affirmative	Negative
I'm going to win.	I'm not going to win.
You're going to win.	You aren't going to win.
He's / She's / It's going to win.	He / She / It isn't going to win.
We're / You're / They're going to win.	We / You / They aren't going to win.

Use

be going to is used to talk about a definite plan to do (or not do) something in the future.

We're going to buy a house.

She isn't going to watch the match.

will and be going to

Use

be going to is used to talk about definite future plans which we have decided. *will* is used to talk about predictions for the future, our ideas and expectations, and things which are not certain.

Plan: **He's going to meet his friends at the football stadium.**

Prediction: **Maybe my team will lose.**

be going to: questions

Questions				Answers
	Am	I		Yes, you are. / No, you aren't.
	Is	he / she / it	going to sleep? going to eat?	Yes, he / she / it is.
				No, he / she / it isn't.
	Are	we / you/ they		Yes, we / you / they are.
				No, we / you / they aren't.
Where	is	she		She's going to sleep in her room.
What	are	we		You're going to eat pizza.

We don't use short forms for positive short answers.

Is he playing today? Yes, he is. NOT ~~Yes, he's.~~

Present continuous for future arrangements

Use

The present continuous is used to describe future events we have decided and fixed.

I'm meeting my friends this evening.

NOT ~~I will meet my friends this evening.~~

They're moving to France in July.

NOT ~~They move to France in July.~~

The present continuous is often used with a time expression.

We're getting married next month / tomorrow.

Indefinite pronouns

We normally use indefinite pronouns with *some-* in positive sentences, and indefinite pronouns with *any-* in negative sentences and questions.

Is anyone here really good at tennis? Yes, someone in my class is school champion.

What did you do last weekend?

I didn't do anything special OR **Nothing special.**

NOT What did you do last weekend? ~~Anything.~~

Use

We use an indefinite pronoun when we don't know, or it's not important, which place, person or thing we are talking about.

Someone left their coat here. I don't know who.

Mike's gone somewhere. I'm not sure where.

Imperatives

1 Match the verbs in A to the words in B. Write affirmative and negative imperative sentences.

A	B
~~listen~~	~~to your teacher~~
not forget	late for school
do	your English
not be	your homework now
practise	to take your keys

Listen to your teacher.

1 _____
2 _____
3 _____
4 _____

be going to

2 Write sentences using *be going to*.

I / race / next year
I'm going to race next year.

1 John / not talk / to us
_____

2 they / play / rugby
_____

3 Dad / drive / to the train station
_____

4 we / not meet / them
_____

5 she / go shopping
_____

6 they / not watch TV
_____

will and be going to

3 Complete the sentences using the correct form of the verbs in brackets.

Plan
We ____'re going to meet____ (meet) the finalists.

1 I _____ (buy) a new bike.
2 She _____ (contact) the journalist.
3 They _____ (watch) TV.

Prediction
4 I think they _____ (be) late.
5 Maybe you _____ (get) a new trainer.
6 He _____ (not be) late.

be going to: questions

4 Write questions using *be going to*. Then write short answers.

she / meet / him ✗
Is she going to meet him? No, she isn't.

1 you / be / late ✓
_____

2 he / watch / a film ✗
_____

3 we / practise / today ✗
_____

4 they / start / at two o'clock ✓
_____

5 Eva / do / her homework ✓
_____

Present continuous for future arrangements

5 Complete the dialogues using the present continuous form of the verbs in the box.

> study ~~do~~ play go not do meet

Amy What ____are____ you ____doing____ on Monday?
Sam I ¹_____ tennis.
Dan ²_____ we _____ to the cinema tonight?
Rob Yes. We ³_____ at seven o'clock.
Sue Are you ⁴_____ this evening?
Ana No, I feel ill. I ⁵_____ anything this evening.

Indefinite pronouns

6 Complete the sentences with the correct indefinite pronouns.

The England manager hasn't got ____anything____ to say about the team's terrible performance.

1 Does _____ here know how to play rugby?
2 We've got _____ new to play our matches. It's a big park near the town centre.
3 _____ happened to Liverpool last season. They played really badly.
4 I don't think there's _____ wrong with Franco. He doesn't look injured.

Modifiers

Modifiers come after the verb *be*. We use them to describe the adjective.

I'm quite good at chess.

Pietro isn't very keen on learning languages.

Present perfect: affirmative and negative

Affirmative	Negative
I have played.	I haven't played.
You have played.	You haven't played.
He has played.	He hasn't played.
She has played.	She hasn't played.
It has played.	It hasn't played.
We have played.	We haven't played.
You have played.	You haven't played.
They have played.	They haven't played.

Note that in spoken and informal written English contracted forms are usually used.

I've had lunch.

He's been to Spain.

Use

Use the present perfect to describe an experience in our lives before now.

I have never touched a snake. (so I don't know what they feel like)

Use the present perfect to describe news or a change in a situation.

She has broken her arm. (so she can't play tennis at the moment)

Don't use the present perfect to say exactly when a past action happened. In this case use the past simple.

I went to Warsaw last week.

NOT *I have been to Warsaw last week.*

Use *ever* and *never* with the present perfect to ask and talk about experiences. *Ever* and *never* come before the past participle.

Have you ever been to Greece? (= at any time in your life)

He has never eaten Chinese food. (= not at any time in his life)

Never means 'not ever'.

I haven't ever done that. (= I've never done that.)

We normally use *ever* with questions, and *never* with positive verbs.

He has never seen the sea.

NOT *He hasn't never seen the sea.*

Present perfect: questions

Questions	Short answers	
	Affirmative	Negative
Have I won?	Yes, I have.	No, I haven't.
Have you won?	Yes, you have.	No, you haven't.
Has he won?	Yes, he has.	No, he hasn't.
Has she won?	Yes, she has.	No, she hasn't.
Has it won?	Yes, it has.	No, it hasn't.
Have we won?	Yes, we have.	No, we haven't.
Have you won?	Yes, you have.	No, you haven't.
Have they won?	Yes, they have.	No, they haven't.

Question words go before the verb *have*.

What have you done?   NOT *What you've done?*

Where has she been?   NOT *Where she's been?*

so and because

Use *so* to give a reason and *because* to explain a result. Use a comma before *so*, but not before *because*.

I was ill, so I didn't go to school.

I wasn't at school because I was ill.

Modifiers

1 Write sentences which are true for you. Use the modifiers in the box.

> ~~not at all~~ a bit quite very really

my family / interested in / extreme sports
<u>My family aren't at all interested in extreme sports.</u>

1 I / good at maths
_____

2 my best friend / scared of spiders
_____

3 I / worried about / the future
_____

4 my friends / keen on / football
_____

Present perfect: affirmative and negative

2 Write the past participles.

want _____<u>wanted</u>_____

1 break	_____	5 do	_____
2 bite	_____	6 swim	_____
3 drive	_____	7 learn	_____
4 fall	_____	8 speak	_____

3 Choose the correct words.

We (haven't) / hasn't been to South America.

1 Simon **have** / **has** bruised his arm.
2 You **haven't** / **hasn't** seen this film.
3 I've / 's driven my uncle's car.
4 She **haven't** / **hasn't** eaten Japanese food.
5 They 've / **has** played tennis.
6 Ella **hasn't** / **haven't** cut her hand.

4 Complete the sentences using the correct form of the verbs in brackets.

We <u>'ve played</u> (play) rugby, but we <u>haven't watched</u> (not watch) a professional match.

1 He _____ (do) all his homework, but he _____ (not finish) reading his book.
2 I _____ (not buy) any clothes, but I _____ (see) some nice trousers.
3 My sister _____ (cook) a cake, but she _____ (not eat) it.

4 Our cat _____ (fall) out of the tree, but it _____ (not break) its leg.
5 I _____ (watch) volleyball on TV, but I _____ (not play) it.
6 She _____ (write) a postcard, but she _____ (send) it yet.

Present perfect: questions

5 Order the words to make questions.

Disneyland / you / to / been / ever / have
<u>Have you ever been to Disneyland?</u>

1 she / ever / has / any / music / composed
_____

2 dog / the / eaten / dinner / its / has
_____

3 country / in / they / lived / another / have
_____

4 tennis / has / he / won / tournament / a / ever
_____

5 we / have / watched / Shrek / this / DVD
_____

6 you / touched / a / snake / ever / have
_____

6 Write questions and short answers using the present perfect.

she / ever / break her arm ✓
<u>Has she ever broken her arm?</u>
<u>Yes, she has.</u>

1 they / ever / meet / a famous actor ✓
_____
_____

2 he / swim / across a lake ✗
_____
_____

3 we / ever / eat / Chinese food ✗
_____
_____

4 you / give / your mother a present ✓
_____
_____

5 she / bruise / her shoulder ✗
_____
_____

6 Carla / visit / the USA ✓
_____
_____

PRONUNCIATION BANK

Unit 1: Third person singular

1 🔘 1.02 Listen to the verbs with the third person singular endings /z/, /s/ and /ɪz/.

/z/	listens	knows	ends	comes
/s/	writes	asks	visits	checks
/ɪz/	organizes	practises	washes	uses

2 🔘 1.03 Listen to the verbs and tick (✓) the correct box.

	/z/	/s/	/ɪz/
changes			✓
finishes			
goes			
likes			
meets			
needs			
watches			
wears			
works			

3 🔘 1.04 Listen again and repeat.

4 Look at the pairs of words. Put a tick (✓) if Word 2 has the same number of syllables as Word 1. Put a cross (✗) if Word 2 has one more syllable.

Word 1	Word 2	Same syllables
bus	buses	✗
need	needs	✓
watch	watches	
plan	plans	
box	boxes	
like	likes	
pass	passes	
key	keys	
carry	carries	

Unit 2: /ə/

1 🔘 1.05 Listen to the sound /ə/ in the words.

1 mirror 3 machine
2 shower 4 furniture

2 🔘 1.06 Listen and tick (✓) the words with the /ə/ sound. Underline syllables with the /ə/ sound.

sofa ✓

1 bed   6 lamp
2 bath   7 microwave
3 picture 8 wardrobe
4 desk   9 bookcase
5 cupboard

3 🔘 1.07 Listen and check your answers. Then listen again and repeat.

4 Look again at exercises 2 and 3. Find six different spellings that have the /ə/ sound.

-or, ____ , ____ , ____ , ____ , ____

Unit 3: Past tense -ed endings

1 🔘 1.08 Listen to the past simple verbs.

/d/	changed	played	used
/t/	practised	helped	looked
/ɪd/	waited	decided	wanted

2 🔘 1.09 Listen to the verbs and tick the correct box.

	/d/	/t/	/ɪd/
counted			✓
graduated			
liked			
needed			
lived			
moved			
started			
ended			
stayed			
watched			
worked			

3 ● 1.10 Listen and check your answers. Then listen again and repeat.

4 Choose the correct options to complete the rule.

The -ed / -ing ending has an extra **syllable / word** when the sound at the end of the verb is / t /, / p /, / z / or / d /.

Unit 4: Weak forms

1 ● 1.11 Listen to the sentences. Notice how the affirmative forms (*was / were*) are weak and the negative forms (*wasn't / weren't*) are stressed.

1 I was sailing.	I wasn't sailing.
2 You were running.	You weren't running.
3 He was climbing.	He wasn't climbing.
4 They were walking.	They weren't walking.

2 ● 1.12 Listen again and repeat the sentences.

3 ● 1.13 Listen to the sentences. Do you hear the weak or the strong forms? Circle the correct words.

We **were** / weren't skiing in France.

James **was** / **wasn't** watching a film.

1 He **was** / **wasn't** swimming across the river.
2 We **were** / **weren't** cycling on holiday.
3 I **was** / **wasn't** having a great time.
4 You **were** / **weren't** using the laptop last night.
5 It **was** / **wasn't** very hot yesterday.

4 ● 1.14 Listen and check your answers. Then listen again and repeat.

5 Do you hear the schwa sound /ə/ in weak or strong forms of *was* and *were*?

Unit 5: Word stress

1 ● 1.15 Listen and repeat the words in the table. Notice the word stress.

●●	●●	●●●	●●●
exam	player	practical	composer

2 ● 1.16 Listen to the words. How many syllables have they got? Write *2* or *3*.

anything _3_

1 artistic	9	player
2 compete	10	practical
3 compose	11	prodigy
4 composer	12	program
5 computer	13	programmer
6 exam	14	remember
7 forget	15	writer
8 painter		

3 Write the words from exercise 2 in the table.

●●	●●	●●●	●●●
exam	player	practical	composer
		anything	

4 ● 1.17 Listen and check your answers. Then listen again and repeat.

5 ● 1.17 Listen again and underline the unstressed syllables which have a schwa /ə/ sound in the table in exercise 3.

play<u>er</u>   practic<u>al</u>

Unit 6: 'll

1 ● 1.18 Listen to the sentences. Which verb form do you hear in each sentence? Tick (✓) A or B.

A	B
They work.	They'll work. ✓
1 I go.	I'll go.
2 We play.	We'll play.
3 I buy.	I'll buy.
4 You win.	You'll win.
5 They live.	They'll live.
6 We study.	We'll study.
7 They travel.	They'll travel.

2 🔊 1.19 Listen and repeat the sentences.

1 We'll go out tomorrow.
2 I'll see you later.
3 She'll become a teacher.
4 You'll marry someone famous.
5 He'll write a book.
6 It'll be a good party.

Unit 7: Recognizing contractions

1 🔊 1.20 Listen to the sentences. You will hear the contractions and the long forms.

1 I've got a new job.   I have got a new job.
2 She's nervous about the exam.   She is nervous about the exam.
3 That's fantastic!   That is fantastic!
4 He's got a new MP3 player.   He has got a new MP3 player.
5 What's your name?   What is your name?
6 That one's better.   That one is better.
7 Who's the song by?   Who is the song by?
8 They're going to move to Toledo.   They are going to move to Toledo.
9 When's your birthday?   When is your birthday?
10 You're the winner.   You are the winner.

2 🔊 1.21 Listen to the sentences. Do you hear the contraction or the long form? Circle the correct words.

(That's) / That is our new teacher.

1 What's / What is it called?
2 You are / You're going to be late again.
3 It has / It's got three bedrooms.
4 They are / They're two years old.
5 Who's / Who is the captain of the football team?
6 Which one's / one is yours?
7 When's / When is the party?
8 She's / She is really intelligent.
9 We have / We've got tickets for a basketball game.

3 🔊 1.22 Listen and check your answers. Then listen again and repeat.

4 Rewrite the sentences with contracted forms. Then count the syllables.

She is at home.   _She's at home._ _3_

1 Peter is feeling ill. _____
2 Bill has got a dog. _____
3 What is happening? _____
4 Maggie is my sister. _____
5 Where is your flat? _____
6 They are great. _____

Unit 8: /ɪ/ and /iː/

1 🔊 1.23 Listen to words with the /ɪ/ and /iː/ sounds.

/ɪ/	/iː/
bin	cheap
bitten	eat
building	feel
give	leave
injure	meet
live	seat
swim	see

2 Put the words in the correct box.

> ~~fish~~ ~~clean~~ meal river hit teach
> wind speak need sink

/ɪ/	/iː/
fish	clean
_____	_____
_____	_____
_____	_____
_____	_____

3 🔊 1.24 Listen and check your answers. Then listen again and repeat.

4 Look again at the words in exercises 1 and 2. What different ways of spelling the /ɪ/ and /iː/ sounds can you find?

/ɪ/ _i (bin)_ _____

/iː/ _____

Phonetic symbols

Vowels

/i/	happy
/ɪ/	it
/iː/	he
/æ/	flag
/ɑː/	art
/e/	egg
/ɜː/	her
/ɒ/	not
/ɔː/	four
/ʊ/	look
/uː/	you
/ə/	sugar
/ʌ/	mum
/eɪ/	day
/aɪ/	why
/ɔɪ/	noisy
/aʊ/	how
/əʊ/	go
/ɪə/	here
/eə/	wear
/ʊə/	tourist

Consonants

/p/	pen
/b/	big
/t/	two
/d/	dog
/k/	can
/g/	good
/tʃ/	beach
/dʒ/	job
/f/	food
/v/	very
/θ/	think
/ð/	then
/s/	speak
/z/	zoo
/ʃ/	she
/ʒ/	television
/h/	house
/m/	meat
/n/	now
/ŋ/	sing
/l/	late
/r/	radio
/j/	yes
/w/	we

Starter unit

aunt (n)   /ɑːnt/
book (n)   /bʊk/
brother (n)   /ˈbrʌðə(r)/
child (n)   /tʃaɪld/
class (n)   /klɑːs/
cousin (n)   /ˈkʌzn/
daughter (n)   /ˈdɔːtə(r)/
difficult (adj)   /ˈdɪfɪkəlt/
English (n)   /ˈɪŋglɪʃ/
exam (n)   /ɪgˈzæm/
exercise (n)   /ˈeksəsaɪz/
family (n)   /ˈfæməli/
fan (n)   /fæn/
father (n)   /ˈfɑːðə(r)/
French (adj)   /frentʃ/
friend (n)   /frend/
geography (n)   /dʒiˈɒgrəfi/
good (adj)   /gʊd/
granddaughter (n)   /ˈgrændɔːtə(r)/
grandfather (n)   /ˈgrænfɑːðə(r)/
grandmother (n)   /ˈgrænmʌðə(r)/
grandparent (n)   /ˈgrænpeərənt/
grandson (n)   /ˈgrænsʌn/
gymnasium (n)   /dʒɪmˈneɪziəm/
history (n)   /ˈhɪstri/
homework (n)   /ˈhəʊmwɜːk/
husband (n)   /ˈhʌzbənd/
ICT (n)   /ˌaɪ ˌsiː ˈtiː/
interesting (adj)   /ˈɪntrəstɪŋ/
laboratory (n)   /ləˈbɒrətri/
maths (n)   /mæθs/
mother (n)   /ˈmʌðə(r)/
music (n)   /ˈmjuːzɪk/
neat (adj)   /niːt/
nephew (n)   /ˈnefjuː/
nice (adj)   /naɪs/
niece (n)   /niːs/
note (n)   /nəʊt/
parent (n)   /ˈpeərənt/
partner (n)   /ˈpɑːtnə(r)/
PE (n)   /ˌpiː ˈiː/
room (n)   /ruːm/
science (n)   /ˈsaɪəns/
sister (n)   /ˈsɪstə(r)/
son (n)   /sʌn/
strict (adj)   /strɪkt/
teacher (n)   /ˈtiːtʃə(r)/
topic (n)   /ˈtɒpɪk/
twin (n)   /twɪn/
wife (n)   /waɪf/
writing (n)   /ˈraɪtɪŋ/

Unit 1

against the rules   /əˈgenst ðə ˌruːlz/
allowed to   /əˈlaʊd tə/
always (adv)   /ˈɔːlweɪz/
arrive (v)   /əˈraɪv/
bag (n)   /bæg/
blog (n)   /blɒg/
bothered (about) (adj)   /ˈbɒðəd/

bowl (n)   /bəʊl/
bus pass (n)   /ˈbʌs ˌpɑːs/
call (v)   /kɔːl/
camel (n)   /ˈkæml/
careful (adj)   /ˈkeəfl/
clothes (n)   /kləʊðz/
collect things (v)   /kəˈlekt ˌθɪŋz/
disorganized (adj)   /dɪsˈɔːgənaɪzd/
go cycling (v)   /ˌgəʊ ˈsaɪklɪŋ/
go shopping (v)   /ˌgəʊ ˈʃɒpɪŋ/
go swimming (v)   /ˌgəʊ ˈswɪmɪŋ/
go to the cinema (v)   /ˌgəʊ tə ðə ˈsɪnəmə/
goat (n)   /gəʊt/
group (n)   /gruːp/
hardly ever (adv)   /ˌhɑːdli ˈevə(r)/
ID card (n)   /ˌaɪ ˈdiː ˌkɑːd/
Japanese (adj)   /dʒæpəˈniːz/
jewellery (n)   /ˈdʒuːəlri/
keen (on) (adj)   /ˈkiːn (ˌɒn)/
keep (v)   /kiːp/
key ring (n)   /ˈkiː ˌrɪŋ/
keys (n)   /kiːz/
laptop (n)   /ˈlæptɒp/
library card (n)   /ˈlaɪbrəri ˌkɑːd/
listen to music (v)   /ˌlɪsn tə ˈmjuːzɪk/
mad (about) (adj)   /ˈmæd (əˌbaʊt)/
magazine (n)   /mægəˈziːn/
make-up (n)   /ˈmeɪk ˌʌp/
manga (n)   /ˈmæŋgə/
meet friends (v)   /ˌmiːt ˈfrendz/
memory (n)   /ˈmeməri/
metal detector (n)   /ˈmetl dɪˌtektə(r)/
mobile phone (n)   /ˌməʊbaɪl ˈfəʊn/
monastery (n)   /ˈmɒnəstri/
money (n)   /ˈmʌni/
monk (n)   /mʌŋk/
MP3 player (n)   /ˌem ˌpiː ˈθriː ˌpleɪə(r)/
never (adv)   /ˈnevə(r)/
novel (n)   /ˈnɒvl/
often (adv)   /ˈɒfn, ˈɒftən/
organized (adj)   /ˈɔːgənaɪzd/
play computer games (v)   /ˌpleɪ kəmˈpjuːtə ˌgeɪmz/
play in a band (v)   /ˌpleɪ ˌɪn ə ˈbænd/
play sport (v)   /ˌpleɪ ˈspɔːt/
possession (n)   /pəˈzeʃn/
purse (n)   /pɜːs/
read magazines and books (v)   /ˌriːd mægəˌziːnz ənd ˈbʊks/
reckon (v)   /ˈrekən/
robes (n)   /rəʊbz/
sandals (n)   /ˈsændlz/
sensible (adj)   /ˈsensəbl/
sentimental (adj)   /sentɪˈmentl/
sometimes (adv)   /ˈsʌmtaɪmz/
study (v)   /ˈstʌdi/
sunglasses (n)   /ˈsʌnglɑːsɪz/
supposed to   /səˈpəʊst tə/

Clothes

jeans · shoes · tracksuit top · trainers · top · tracksuit bottoms · pullover · T-shirt · cap · shorts · coat · socks

surf the internet (v)   /ˌsɜːf ði ˈɪntənet/
take photos (v)   /ˌteɪk ˈfəʊtəʊz/
tent (n)   /tent/
ticket (n)   /ˈtɪkɪt/
tie (n)   /taɪ/
trendy (adj)   /ˈtrendi/
umbrella (n)   /ʌmˈbrelə/
usually (adv)   /ˈjuːʒuəli/
wallet (n)   /ˈwɒlɪt/
watch (n)   /wɒtʃ/
watch TV (v)   /ˌwɒtʃ ˌtiː ˈviː/

Unit 2

amazing (adj)   /əˈmeɪzɪŋ/
argue (v)   /ˈɑːgjuː/
armchair (n)   /ˈɑːmtʃeə(r)/
balcony (n)   /ˈbælkəni/
bath (n)   /bɑːθ/
bed (n)   /bed/
behind (prep)   /bɪˈhaɪnd/
between (prep)   /bɪˈtwiːn/
bookcase (n)   /ˈbʊkkeɪs/
breakfast (n)   /ˈbrekfəst/

busy (adj)   /ˈbɪzi/
cathedral (n)   /kəˈθiːdrəl/
celebrity (n)   /səˈlebrəti/
chair (n)   /tʃeə(r)/
chest of drawers (n)   /ˌtʃest əv ˈdrɔːz/
clean the car (v)   /ˌkliːn ðə ˈkɑː(r)/
clean the floor (v)   /ˌkliːn ðə ˈflɔː(r)/
clear the table (v)   /ˌklɪə ðə ˈteɪbl/
climb (v)   /klaɪm/
convertible (n)   /kənˈvɜːtəbl/

Homes

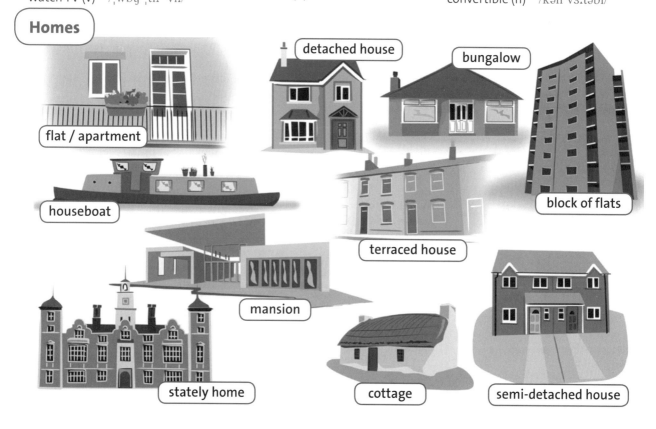

flat / apartment · detached house · bungalow · houseboat · terraced house · block of flats · mansion · stately home · cottage · semi-detached house

cry (v) /kraɪ/
cupboard (n) /'kʌbəd/
describe (v) /dɪ'skraɪb/
desk (n) /desk/
dinner (n) /'dɪnə(r)/
do the ironing (v) /ˌduː ði 'aɪənɪŋ/
do the shopping (v) /ˌduː ðə 'ʃɒpɪŋ/
do the vacuuming (v) /ˌduː ðə 'vækjuəmɪŋ/
do the washing-up (v) /ˌduː ðə ˌwɒʃɪŋ 'ʌp/
furniture (n) /'fɜːnɪtʃə(r)/
glass (n) /glɑːs/
help (v) /help/
holiday home (n) /'hɒlədeɪ ˌhəʊm/
ideal (adj) /aɪ'diːəl/
in front of (prep) /ˌɪn 'frʌnt əv/
lamp (n) /læmp/
living room (n) /'lɪvɪŋ ˌruːm/
look (v) /lʊk/
lunch (n) /lʌntʃ/
make your bed (v) /ˌmeɪk ˌjɔː 'bed/
microwave (n) /'maɪkrəweɪv/
mirror (n) /'mɪrə(r)/
modern (adj) /'mɒdn/
near (prep) /nɪə(r)/
next to (prep) /'neks ˌtuː, tə/
on (prep) /ɒn/

outside (prep) /aʊt'saɪd/
phone (v) /fəʊn/
picture (n) /'pɪktʃə(r)/
questionnaire (n) /ˌkwestʃə'neə(r)/
rain (v) /reɪn/
run around (v) /ˌrʌn ə'raʊnd/
sea (n) /siː/
shower (n) /'ʃaʊə(r)/
sleep (v) /sliːp/
sofa (n) /'səʊfə/
suppose (v) /sə'pəʊz/
swim (v) /swɪm/
table (n) /'teɪbl/
take out the rubbish (v) /ˌteɪk ˌaʊt ðə 'rʌbɪʃ/
take the dog for a walk (v) /ˌteɪk ðə 'dɒg fər ə ˌwɔːk/
tidy / clean your room (v) /ˌtaɪdi, ˌkliːn ˌjɔː 'ruːm/
tour (n) /tʊə(r)/
traditional (adj) /trə'dɪʃənəl/
under (prep) /'ʌndə(r)/
view (n) /vjuː/
wardrobe (n) /'wɔːdrəʊb/
wash (v) /wɒʃ/
washing machine (n) /'wɒʃɪŋ məˌʃiːn/
window (n) /'wɪndəʊ/
write (v) /raɪt/

Unit 3

adopt (v) /ə'dɒpt/
after (that) (adv) /ˌɑːftə '(ðæt)/
afternoon (n) /ˌɑːftə'nuːn/
angry (adj) /'æŋgri/
baby (n) /'beɪbi/
be born (v) /ˌbi 'bɔːn/
become a professional (v) /bɪˌkʌm ə prə'feʃənl/
become rich (v) /bɪˌkʌm 'rɪtʃ/
boring (adj) /'bɔːrɪŋ/
buy a house (v) /ˌbaɪ ə 'haʊs/
camera (n) /'kæmərə/
celebrate (v) /'seləbreɪt/
ceremony (n) /'serəməni/
cute (adj) /kjuːt/
day (n) /deɪ/
dentist (n) /'dentɪst/
do an exam (v) /ˌduː ən ɪg'zæm/
draw (v) /drɔː/
dream (n) /driːm/
evening (n) /'iːvnɪŋ/
finally (adv) /'faɪnəli/
first (adj) /fɜːst/
forget (v) /fə'get/
from memory /frəm 'meməri/
funny (adj) /'fʌni/
get a job (v) /ˌget ə 'dʒɒb/
get married (v) /ˌget 'mærid/

Transport

underground
lorry
car
bus
moped / scooter
tram
plane
train
bike
boat
coach
motorbike

graduate from university (v)
/ˌgrædʒueɪt frəm juːnɪˈvɜːsəti/
grow up (v)   /ˌgrəʊ ˈʌp/
handball (n)   /ˈhændbɔːl/
have a child (v)   /ˌhæv ə ˈtʃaɪld/
helicopter (n)   /ˈhelɪkɒptə(r)/
human (adj)   /ˈhjuːmən/
immediately (adv)   /ɪˈmiːdiətli/
joke (n)   /dʒəʊk/
last (adv, adj)   /lɑːst/
learn to drive (v)   /ˌlɜːn tə ˈdraɪv/
leave home (v)   /ˌliːv ˈhəʊm/
leave school (v)   /ˌliːv ˈskuːl/
lonely   /ˈləʊnli/
lucky (adj)   /ˈlʌki/
meal (n)   /miːl/
medical school (n)   /ˈmedɪkl ˌskuːl/
memorable (adj)   /ˈmemərəbl/
memorize (v)   /ˈmeməraɪz/
memory (n)   /ˈmeməri/
morning (n)   /ˈmɔːnɪŋ/
move to another country (v)
/ˌmuːv tu əˌnʌðə ˈkʌntri/
naughty (adj)   /ˈnɔːti/
nervous (adj)   /ˈnɜːvəs/
pack (n)   /pæk/
party (n)   /ˈpɑːti/

photographic memory (n)
/ˌfəʊtəˌgræfɪk ˈmeməri/
playing cards (n)   /ˈpleɪɪŋ ˌkɑːdz/
recite (v)   /rɪˈsaɪt/
remember (v)   /rɪˈmembə(r)/
repeat (v)   /rɪˈpiːt/
scary (adj)   /ˈskeəri/
start a company (v)   /ˌstɑːt ə
ˈkʌmpəni/
strange (adj)   /streɪndʒ/
teddy bear (n)   /ˈtedi ˌbeə(r)/
then (adv)   /ðen/
toy (n)   /tɔɪ/
train (v)   /treɪn/
upset (adj)   /ʌpˈset/
visit (n)   /ˈvɪzɪt/
wake up (v)   /ˌweɪk ˈʌp/
win a competition (v)   /ˌwɪn ə
kɒmpəˈtɪʃn/

Unit 4

across (prep)   /əˈkrɒs/
as soon as (adv)   /əz ˈsuːn əz/
back (n)   /bæk/
barrel (n)   /ˈbærəl/
base jumping (n)   /ˈbeɪs ˌdʒʌmpɪŋ/

beach (n)   /biːtʃ/
brave (adj)   /breɪv/
cheer (v)   /tʃɪə(r)/
climb (v)   /klaɪm/
coal (n)   /kəʊl/
cook (v)   /kʊk/
copy (v)   /ˈkɒpi/
crash (v)   /kræʃ/
crowd (n)   /kraʊd/
cycle (v)   /ˈsaɪkl/
dangerous (adj)   /ˈdeɪndʒərəs/
dare (v)   /deə(r)/
daring (adj)   /ˈdeərɪŋ/
daredevil (n)   /ˈdeədevl/
desert (n)   /ˈdezət/
dive (v)   /daɪv/
diver (n)   /ˈdaɪvə(r)/
diving board (n)   /ˈdaɪvɪŋ ˌbɔːd/
down (prep)   /daʊn/
egg (n)   /eg/
expect (v)   /ɪkˈspekt/
fall (v)   /fɔːl/
falls (n)   /fɔːlz/
fly (v)   /flaɪ/
forest (n)   /ˈfɒrɪst/
happen (v)   /ˈhæpən/
helmet (n)   /ˈhelmɪt/

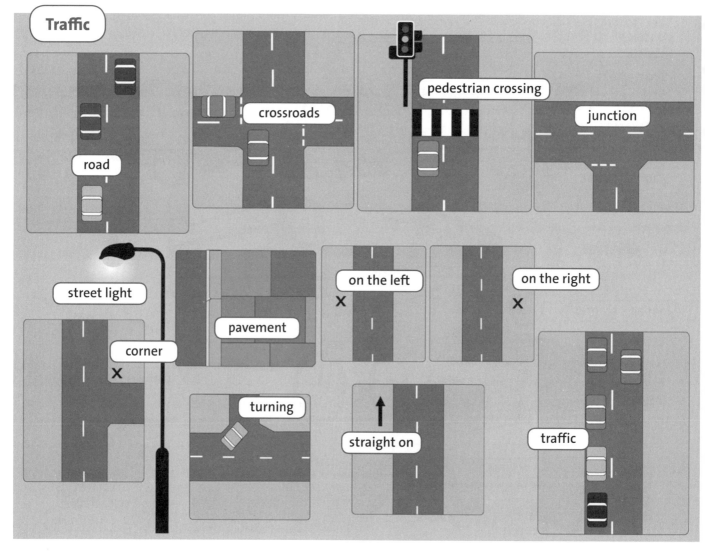

hero (n) /ˈhɪərəʊ/
heroine (n) /ˈherəʊɪn/
into (prep) /ˈɪntuː, ˈɪntə/
invent (v) /ɪnˈvent/
jump (v) /dʒʌmp/
kind (adj) /kaɪnd/
lake (n) /leɪk/
litre (n) /ˈliːtə(r)/
meet (v) /miːt/
mountains (n) /ˈmaʊntɪnz/
ocean (n) /ˈəʊʃn/
off (prep) /ɒf/
over (prep) /ˈəʊvə(r)/
parachute (n) /ˈpærəʃuːt/
piranha (n) /pɪˈrɑːnə/
pole (n) /pəʊl/
practise (v) /ˈpræktɪs/
prohibit (n) /prəˈhɪbɪt/
pyramid (n) /ˈpɪrəmɪd/
rescue (n) /ˈreskjuː/
river (n) /ˈrɪvə(r)/
rock (n) /rɒk/
rope (n) /rəʊp/
sail (v) /seɪl/
shark (n) /ʃɑːk/
site (n) /saɪt/
skateboard (n) /ˈskeɪtbɔːd/
skis (n) /skiːz/
spectacular (adj) /spekˈtækjʊlə/
stairs (n) /steəz/
stand (v) /stænd/
stunt (n) /stʌnt/
surfboard (n) /ˈsɜːfbɔːd/
surfer (n) /ˈsɜːfə(r)/

swim (v) /swɪm/
swimming shorts (n) /ˈswɪmɪŋ ʃɔːts/
through (prep) /θruː/
tightrope (n) /ˈtaɪtrəʊp/
towards (prep) /təˈwɔːdz/
trick (n) /trɪk/
under (prep) /ˈʌndə(r)/
up (prep) /ʌp/
valley (n) /ˈvæli/
walk (v) /wɔːk/
wave (n) /weɪv/
well done! (exc) /ˌwel ˈdʌn/
you're kidding! (exc) /ˌjɔː ˈkɪdɪŋ/

Unit 5

act (v) /ækt/
actor (n) /ˈæktə(r)/
aggressive (adj) /əˈgresɪv/
artistic (adj) /ɑːˈtɪstɪk/
bear (n) /beə(r)/
beautiful (adj) /ˈbjuːtɪfl/
break a record (v) /ˌbreɪk ə ˈrekɔːd/
brush your teeth (v) /ˌbrʌʃ jɔː ˈtiːθ/
butterfly (n) /ˈbʌtəflaɪ/
chemistry (n) /ˈkemɪstri/
chess (n) /tʃes/
common (adj) /ˈkɒmən/
compete (v) /kəmˈpiːt/
competition (n) /kɒmpəˈtɪʃn/
competitor (n) /kəmˈpetɪtə(r)/
compose (v) /kəmˈpəʊz/

composer (n) /kəmˈpəʊzə(r)/
conference (n) /ˈkɒnfərəns/
cook (n, v) /kʊk/
dance (n) /dɑːns/
dance (v) /dɑːns/
dancer (n) /ˈdɑːnsə(r)/
decision (n) /dɪˈsɪʒn/
destruction (n) /dɪˈstrʌkʃn/
detective (n) /dɪˈtektɪv/
dog (n) /dɒg/
dolphin (n) /ˈdɒlfɪn/
domesticated (adj) /dəˈmestɪkeɪtɪd/
elephant (n) /ˈelɪfənt/
encourage (v) /ɪnˈkʌrɪdʒ/
enemy (n) /ˈenəmi/
far (adj) /fɑː(r)/
fast (adj) /fɑːst/
fish (n) /fɪʃ/
fluently (adv) /ˈfluːəntli/
fly (n) /flaɪ/
football player (n) /ˈfʊtbɔːl ˌpleɪə(r)/
frog (n) /frɒg/
hard (adv) /hɑːd/
hear (v) /hɪə(r)/
heavy (adj) /ˈhevi/
however (adv) /haʊˈevə(r)/
hunt (v) /hʌnt/
imagine (v) /ɪˈmædʒɪn/
intelligent (adj) /ɪnˈtelɪdʒənt/
invent (v) /ɪnˈvent/
inventor (n) /ɪnˈventə(r)/
karate (n) /kəˈrɑːti/
king (n) /kɪŋ/

Entertainment

ballet
stage
programme
opera
concert
film
ticket
seat
row
musical
play

light (adj)   /laɪt/
make a decision (v)   /ˌmeɪk ə dɪˈsɪʒn/
make friends (v)   /ˌmeɪk ˈfrendz/
monkey (n)   /ˈmʌŋki/
noisy (adj)   /ˈnɔɪzi/
octopus (n)   /ˈɒktəpəs/
paint (v)   /peɪnt/
painter (n)   /ˈpeɪntə(r)/
parrot (n)   /ˈpærət/
peaceful (adj)   /ˈpiːsfl/
pig (n)   /pɪg/
polio (n)   /ˈpəʊliəʊ/
poster (n)   /ˈpəʊstə(r)/
practical (adj)   /ˈpræktɪkl/
prince (n)   /prɪns/
prodigy (n)   /ˈprɒdədʒi/
programme (v)   /ˈprəʊgræm/
programmer (n)   /ˈprəʊgræmə(r)/
queen (n)   /kwiːn/
rare (adj)   /reə(r)/
ride a bike (v)   /ˌraɪd ə ˈbaɪk/
shout (v)   /ʃaʊt/
sing (v)   /sɪŋ/
singer (n)   /ˈsɪŋə(r)/
slow (adj)   /sləʊ/
solar energy (n)   /ˌsəʊlər ˈenədʒi/
spell (v)   /spel/
start university (v)   /ˌstɑːt juːnɪˈvɜːsəti/
stupid (adj)   /ˈstjuːpɪd/
swim (v)   /swɪm/
swimmer (n)   /ˈswɪmə/
table tennis (n)   /ˈteɪbl ˌtenɪs/
take a break (v)   /ˌteɪk ə ˈbreɪk/

take an exam (v)   /ˌteɪk ən ɪgˈzæm/
talent (n)   /ˈtælənt/
teenager (n)   /ˈtiːneɪdʒə(r)/
though (adv)   /ðəʊ/
underwater (adv)   /ˌʌndəˈwɔːtə(r)/
whale (n)   /weɪl/
wild (adj)   /waɪld/
win (v)   /wɪn/
winner (n)   /ˈwɪnə(r)/
writer (n)   /ˈraɪtə(r)/

Unit 6

a few (det)   /ə ˈfjuː/
agree (with sb) (v)   /əˈgriː/
ambitious (adj)   /æmˈbɪʃəs/
approximate (adj)   /əˈprɒksɪmət/
arrogant (adj)   /ˈærəgənt/
average (adj)   /ˈævərɪdʒ/
bet (v)   /bet/
billion (n)   /ˈbɪljən/
button (n)   /ˈbʌtn/
century (n)   /ˈsentʃəri/
couple (n)   /ˈkʌpl/
creative (adj)   /kriˈeɪtɪv/
death (n)   /deθ/
decade (n)   /ˈdekeɪd/
definitely (adv)   /ˈdefɪnətli/
disagree (with sb) (v)   /dɪsəˈgriː/
dozen (n)   /ˈdʌzn/
easy-going (adj)   /ˌiːzi ˈgəʊɪŋ/
everybody (pron)   /ˈevribɒdi/
exist (v)   /ɪgˈzɪst/
fear (n)   /fɪə(r)/
fortune (n)   /ˈfɔːtʃuːn/

friendly (adj)   /ˈfrendli/
generous (adj)   /ˈdʒenərəs/
half (n)   /hɑːf/
helpful (adj)   /ˈhelpfl/
hour (n)   /ˈaʊə(r)/
hundred (n)   /ˈhʌndrəd/
Iceland (n)   /ˈaɪslənd/
impatient (adj)   /ɪmˈpeɪʃnt/
Ireland (n)   /ˈaɪələnd/
key (n)   /kiː/
kilometre (n)   /ˈkɪləmiːtə(r), kɪˈlɒmɪtə(r)/
Korea (n)   /kəˈrɪə/
Last Supper (n)   /ˌlɑːst ˈsʌpə(r)/
marathon (n)   /ˈmærəθən/
mean (adj)   /miːn/
millennium (n)   /mɪˈleniəm/
millimetre (n)   /ˈmɪlimiːtə(r)/
million (n)   /ˈmɪljən/
minute (n)   /ˈmɪnɪt/
modest (adj)   /ˈmɒdɪst/
month (n)   /mʌnθ/
moody (adj)   /ˈmuːdi/
negative (adj)   /ˈnegətɪv/
nobody (pron)   /ˈnəʊbədi/
nought (n)   /nɔːt/
outgoing (adj)   /aʊtˈgəʊɪŋ/
patient (adj)   /ˈpeɪʃnt/
planet (n)   /ˈplænɪt/
positive (adj)   /ˈpɒzətɪv/
prosperity (n)   /prɒˈsperəti/
quarter (n)   /ˈkwɔːtə(r)/
Russia (n)   /ˈrʌʃə/
second (n)   /ˈsekənd/
serious (adj)   /ˈsɪəriəs/

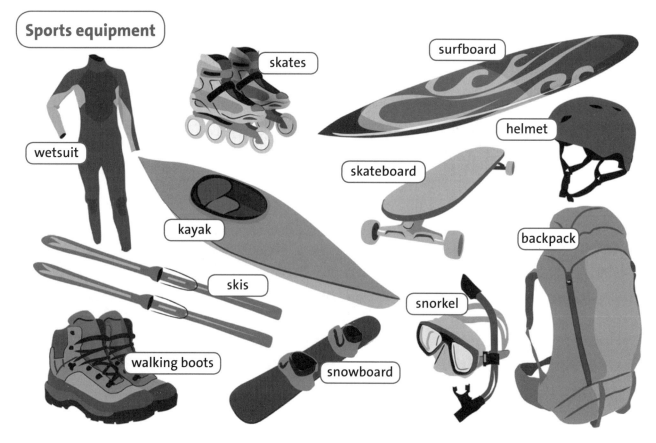

Sports equipment

skates
surfboard
wetsuit
helmet
skateboard
kayak
backpack
skis
snorkel
walking boots
snowboard

shy (adj) /ʃaɪ/
space travel (n) /'speɪs ˌtrævl/
superstition (n) /suːpə'stɪʃn/
superstitious (adj) /suːpə'stɪʃəs/
thousand (n) /'θaʊznd/
triskaidekophobia (n)
  /trɪskaɪdekə'fəʊbiə/
Turkey (n) /'tɜːki/
unambitious (adj) /ʌnæm'bɪʃəs/
unfriendly (adj) /ʌn'frendli/
unhelpful (adj) /ʌn'helpfl/
unimaginative (adj)
  /ʌnɪ'mædʒɪnətɪv/
unlucky (adj) /ʌn'lʌki/
week (n) /wiːk/
year (n) /jɪə(r)/

Unit 7

accept (v) /ək'sept/
athletics (n) /æθ'letɪks/
atmosphere (n) /'ætməsfɪə(r)/
basketball (n) /'bɑːskɪtbɔːl/
captain (n) /'kæptɪn/
champion (n) /'tʃæmpiən/
compete (v) /kəm'piːt/
contact (v) /'kɒntækt/
court (n) /kɔːt/
cycling (n) /'saɪklɪŋ/
disabled (adj) /dɪs'eɪbled/

fewer (adj) /'fjuːə(r)/
finalist (n) /'faɪnəlɪst/
find (v) /faɪnd/
football (n) /'fʊtbɔːl/
formal (adj) /'fɔːml/
Formula 1, Formula 3 (n)
  /ˌfɔːmjələ 'wʌn, ˌfɔːmjələ 'θriː/
have a go at (v) /'hæv ə ˌgəʊ ət/
informal (adj) /ɪn'fɔːml/
instructor (n) /ɪn'strʌktə(r)/
journalist (n) /'dʒɜːnəlɪst/
kart (n) /kɑːt/
look forward (to doing sth) (v)
  /ˌlʊk 'fɔːwəd/
loser (n) /'luːzə(r)/
manager (n) /'mænɪdʒə(r)/
match (n) /mætʃ/
motocross (n) /'məʊtəkrɒs/
off-road (adj) /ˌɒf 'rəʊd/
owner (n) /'əʊnə(r)/
pitch (n) /pɪtʃ/
plan (v) /plæn/
player (n) /'pleɪə(r)/
race (n) /reɪs/
racing (n) /'reɪsɪŋ/
rally car (n) /'ræli ˌkɑː(r)/
referee (n) /refə'riː/
rugby (n) /'rʌgbi/
running (n) /'rʌnɪŋ/

season (n) /'siːzn/
shoe (n) /ʃuː/
situation (n) /sɪtʃu'eɪʃn/
skiing (n) /'skiːɪŋ/
smoke (v) /sməʊk/
sponsor (n) /'spɒnsə(r)/
stadium (n) /'steɪdiəm/
support (v) /sə'pɔːt/
supporter (n) /sə'pɔːtə(r)/
team (n) /tiːm/
tennis (n) /'tenɪs/
tournament (n) /'tʊənəmənt/
trainer (n) /'treɪnə(r)/
trophy (n) /'trəʊfi/
TV reporter (n) /ˌtiː 'viː rɪˌpɔːtə(r)/
Yours faithfully /ˌjɔːz 'feɪθfəli/

Unit 8

ambulance (n) /'æmbjələns/
ankle (n) /'æŋkl/
arachnophobia (n)
  /əræknə'fəʊbiə/
arm (n) /ɑːm/
bad (at) (adj) /'bæd (ˌæt, ət)/
banana (n) /bə'nɑːnə/
bite (n) /baɪt/
bone (n) /bəʊn/
broken (past part) /'brəʊkən/
bruise (v, n) /bruːz/

First aid

bandage

ice

plaster

ambulance

paramedic

AMBULANCE

crutches

sling

ASPIRIN

stretcher

builder (n) /ˈbɪldə(r)/
burn (v, n) /bɜːn/
burnt (past part) /bɜːnt/
chess (n) /tʃes/
claustrophobia (n)
/ˌklɔːstrəˈfəʊbiə/
construction worker (n)
/kənˈstrʌkʃn ˌwɜːkə(r)/
curry (n) /ˈkʌri/
cut (v, n) /kʌt/
danger (n) /ˈdeɪndʒə(r)/
dark (adj) /dɑːk/
diary (n) /ˈdaɪəri/
documentary (n) /dɒkjuˈmentri/
elbow (n) /ˈelbəʊ/
enthusiastic (about) (adj)
/ɪnθjuːziˈæstɪk/
exotic (adj) /ɪɡˈzɒtɪk/
exposure therapy (n)
/ɪkˈspəʊʒə ˌθerəpi/
fall down / over (v) /ˌfɔːl ˈdaʊn,
ˈəʊvə(r)/
farming (n) /ˈfɑːmɪŋ/
finger (n) /ˈfɪŋɡə(r)/
firefighter (n) /ˈfaɪəfaɪtə(r)/
fishing (n) /ˈfɪʃɪŋ/
fond (of) (adj) /ˈfɒnd (əv)/
foot (n) /fʊt/
frightened (of) (adj) /ˈfraɪtnd (əv)/
Guess what! (exc) /ˌɡes ˈwɒt/
hand (n) /hænd/
happy (about) (adj) /ˈhæpi (əˌbaʊt)/
head (n) /hed/
hide (v) /haɪd/
hospital (n) /ˈhɒspɪtl/
How's it going? /ˌhaʊz ˌɪt ˈɡəʊɪŋ/
hurry (v) /ˈhʌri/
illegal (adj) /ɪˈliːɡl/
in public (adv) /ɪn ˈpʌblɪk/
injure (v) /ˈɪndʒə(r)/
injury (n) /ˈɪndʒəri/
insect (n) /ˈɪnsekt/
interested (in) (adj) /ˈɪntrəstɪd (ˌɪn)/
kick (v) /kɪk/
knee (n) /niː/
land (v) /lænd/
leg (n) /leɡ/
move (v) /muːv/
neck (n) /nek/
need (v) /niːd/
neither (adv) /ˈnaɪðə(r), ˈniːðə(r)/
nose (n) /nəʊz/
paramedic (n) /pærəˈmedɪk/
phobia (n) /ˈfəʊbiə/
phobic (adj) /ˈfəʊbɪk/
pilot (n) /ˈpaɪlət/
plastic (adj) /ˈplæstɪk/
police officer (n) /pəˈliːs ˌɒfɪsə(r)/
president (n) /ˈprezɪdənt/
racing driver (n) /ˈreɪsɪŋ ˌdraɪvə(r)/
real (adj) /ˈriːəl/
ridiculous (adj) /rɪˈdɪkjələs/
risk (n) /rɪsk/

roller coaster (n) /ˈrəʊlə
ˌkəʊstə(r)/
save (v) /seɪv/
scared (of) (adj) /ˈskeəd (əv)/
score (v) /skɔː(r)/
scorpion (n) /ˈskɔːpiən/
See you! /ˈsiː ˌjuː/
send (v) /send/
series (n) /ˈsɪəriːz/
shoulder (n) /ˈʃəʊldə(r)/
side (n) /saɪd/
snake (n) /sneɪk/
specialist (n) /ˈspeʃəlɪst/
spicy (adj) /ˈspaɪsi/
spider (n) /ˈspaɪdə(r)/
sprain (v, n) /spreɪn/
storm (n) /stɔːm/
stressed-out (about) (adj) /ˌstrest
ˈaʊt (əˌbaʊt)/
stunt man / woman (n) /ˈstʌnt
ˌmæn, ˌwʊmən/
terrified (of) (adj) /ˈterɪfaɪd (əv)/
throw (v) /θrəʊ/
thunderstorm (n) /ˈθʌndəstɔːm/
toe (n) /təʊ/
touch (v) /tʌtʃ/
unpleasant (adj) /ʌnˈpleznt/
volcano (n) /vɒlˈkeɪnəʊ/
weird (adj) /wɪəd/
What's wrong? /ˌwɒts ˈrɒŋ/
worried (about) (adj) /ˈwʌrid
(əˌbaʊt)/
wrist (n) /rɪst/

English Plus Options

Extra listening and speaking

Unit 1
drama (n) /ˈdrɑːmə/
horse riding (n) /ˈhɔːs ˌraɪdɪŋ/
judo (n) /ˈdʒuːdəʊ/
scuba diving (n) /ˈskuːbə ˌdaɪvɪŋ/

Unit 2
orange (n) /ˈɒrɪndʒ/
sink (n) /sɪŋk/

Unit 3
crisp (n) /krɪsp/
snack (n) /snæk/

Unit 4
crossing (n) /ˈkrɒsɪŋ/
light (n) /laɪt/
pedestrian (n) /pəˈdestriən/
secondary (adj) /ˈsekəndri/
stop (n) /stɒp/
straight on (adv) /ˌstreɪt ˈɒn/
youth (n) /juːθ/

Unit 5
ballet (n) /ˈbæleɪ/

front (n) /frʌnt/
middle (n) /ˈmɪdl/
musical (n) /ˈmjuːzɪkl/
play (n) /pleɪ/
row (n) /rəʊ/
show (n) /ʃəʊ/
ticket (n) /ˈtɪkɪt/

Unit 6
cost (v) /kɒst/
price (n) /praɪs/

Unit 7
draw (n) /drɔː/
goal (n) /ɡəʊl/
lose (v) /luːz/
nil (n) /nɪl/

Unit 8
aspirin (n) /ˈæsprɪn/
bandage (n) /ˈbændɪdʒ/
plaster (n) /ˈplɑːstə(r)/

Curriculum extra

Unit 1
advertising (n) /ˈædvətaɪzɪŋ/
attractive (adj) /əˈtræktɪv/
basic (adj) /ˈbeɪsɪk/
brand (n) /brænd/
cheap (adj) /tʃiːp/
company (n) /ˈkʌmpəni/
designer label (n) /dɪˈzaɪnə ˌleɪbl/
essential (adj) /ɪˈsenʃl/
food (n) /fuːd/
glasses (n) /ˈɡlɑːsɪz/
non-essential (adj) /ˌnɒn ɪˈsenʃl/
similar (adj) /ˈsɪmələ(r)/
trainers (n) /ˈtreɪnəz/

Unit 2
attack (n) /əˈtæk/
forever (adv) /fərˈevə(r)/
grow (v) /ɡrəʊ/
journey (n) /ˈdʒɜːni/
metaphor (n) /ˈmetəfə(r)/
poem (n) /ˈpəʊɪm/
rhyme (v) /raɪm/
road (n) /rəʊd/
safe (adj) /seɪf/
syllable (n) /ˈsɪləbl/
tunnel (n) /ˈtʌnl/
verse (n) /vɜːs/

Unit 3
bird (n) /bɜːd/
colourful (adj) /ˈkʌləfl/
folk story (n) /ˈfəʊk ˌstɔːri/
jungle (n) /ˈdʒʌŋɡl/
lost (adj) /lɒst/
moral (n) /ˈmɒrəl/
narrator (n) /nəˈreɪtə(r)/
net (n) /net/
recognize (v) /ˈrekəɡnaɪz/

Unit 4

cause (v) /kɔːz/
course (n) /kɔːs/
erosion (n) /ɪˈrəʊʒn/
estuary (n) /ˈestʃuəri/
flat (adj) /flæt/
meander (n) /miˈændə(r)/
mouth (n) /maʊθ/
salty (adj) /ˈsɔːlti/
source (n) /sɔːs/
steep (adj) /stiːp/
valley (n) /ˈvæli/
waterfall (n) /ˈwɔːtəfɔːl/
wide (adj) /waɪd/

Unit 5

adapt (v) /əˈdæpt/
appearance (n) /əˈpɪərəns/
arctic fox (n) /ˌɑːktɪk ˈfɒks/
arctic tern (n) /ˌɑːktɪk ˈtɜːn/
breed (v) /briːd/
cobra (n) /ˈkəʊbrə/
feed (v) /fiːd/
grey whale (n) /ˌɡreɪ ˈweɪl/
habitat (n) /ˈhæbɪtæt/
migrate (v) /maɪˈɡreɪt/
migration (n) /maɪˈɡreɪʃn/
phenomenon (n) /fəˈnɒmɪnən/
salmon (n) /ˈsæmən/
substance (n) /ˈsʌbstəns/
venom (n) /ˈvenəm/

Unit 6

chart (n) /tʃɑːt/
chocolate bar (n) /ˈtʃɒklət ˌbɑː(r)/
data (n) /ˈdeɪtə/
fruit (n) /fruːt/
healthy (adj) /ˈhelθi/
record (v) /rɪˈkɔːd/
result (n) /rɪˈzʌlt/
survey (n) /ˈsɜːveɪ/

Unit 7

calculate (v) /ˈkælkjəleɪt/
circuit (n) /ˈsɜːkɪt/
equation (n) /ɪˈkweɪʒn/
lap (n) /læp/
speed (n) /spiːd/
speedway (n) /ˈspiːdweɪ/

Unit 8

afraid (adj) /əˈfreɪd/
castle (n) /ˈkɑːsl/
coach (n) /kəʊtʃ/
cottage (n) /ˈkɒtɪdʒ/
description (n) /dɪˈskrɪpʃn/
dialogue (n) /ˈdaɪəlɒɡ/
dressed (adj) /drest/
face (n) /feɪs/
go back (v) /ˌɡəʊ ˈbæk/
howl (v) /haʊl/
laugh (v) /lɑːf/
narration (n) /nəˈreɪʃn/
narrow (adj) /ˈnærəʊ/
no longer (adv) /ˌnəʊ ˈlɒŋɡə(r)/
pull (v) /pʊl/

roar (v) /rɔː(r)/
silent (adj) /ˈsaɪlənt/
suddenly (adv) /ˈsʌdənli/
taxi (n) /ˈtæksi/
train (n) /treɪn/
wolf (n) /wʊlf/

Culture

Unit 1

babysitting (n) /ˈbeɪbisɪtɪŋ/
deliver (v) /dɪˈlɪvə(r)/
newspaper (n) /ˈnjuːzpeɪpə(r)/
part-time job (n) /ˌpɑːt ˌtaɪm ˈdʒɒb/
pocket money (n) /ˈpɒkɪt ˌmʌni/
spend (v) /spend/

Unit 2

country (n) /ˈkʌntri/
tower block (n) /ˈtaʊə ˌblɒk/

Unit 3

bandage (v) /ˈbændɪdʒ/
cassette (n) /kəˈset/
clearly (adv) /ˈklɪəli/
disco (n) /ˈdɪskəʊ/
housewife (n) /ˈhaʊswaɪf/
movie (n) /ˈmuːvi/
radio station (n) /ˈreɪdiəʊ ˌsteɪʃn/
rock and roll (n) /ˌrɒk ən ˈrəʊl/
type (n) /taɪp/

Unit 4

activity (n) /ækˈtɪvəti/
adventure sport (n) /ədˈventʃə ˌspɔːt/
attract (v) /əˈtrækt/
bungee-jumping (n) /ˈbʌndʒi ˌdʒʌmpɪŋ/
combine (v) /kəmˈbaɪn/
fresh (adj) /freʃ/
hang-gliding (n) /ˈhæŋ ˌɡlaɪdɪŋ/
hiking (n) /ˈhaɪkɪŋ/
jet-boating (n) /ˈdʒet ˌbəʊtɪŋ/
mountain biking (n) /ˈmaʊntən ˌbaɪkɪŋ/
paragliding (n) /ˈpærəɡlaɪdɪŋ/
quiet (adj) /ˈkwaɪət/
scare (v) /skeə(r)/
skydiving (n) /ˈskaɪdaɪvɪŋ/
slowly (adv) /ˈsləʊli/
sunset (n) /ˈsʌnset/
vegetable (n) /ˈvedʒtəbl/
white-water rafting (n) /ˌwaɪt ˌwɔːtə ˈrɑːftɪŋ/

Unit 5

Aboriginal (adj) /æbəˈrɪdʒənl/
achievement (n) /əˈtʃiːvmənt/
award (n) /əˈwɔːd/
barbecue (n) /ˈbɑːbɪkjuː/
bonfire (n) /ˈbɒnfaɪə(r)/
cricket (n) /ˈkrɪkɪt/
date (n) /deɪt/
event (n) /ɪˈvent/

fair (n) /feə(r)/
festival (n) /ˈfestɪvl/
land (n) /lænd/
New Zealand (n) /ˌnjuː ˈziːlənd/
opportunity (n) /ɒpəˈtjuːnəti/
organize (v) /ˈɔːɡənaɪz/
politician (n) /pɒləˈtɪʃn/
scientist (n) /ˈsaɪəntɪst/
traditional (adj) /trəˈdɪʃənl/

Unit 6

European Union (n) /ˌjʊərəˌpiːən ˈjuːniən/
extreme (adj) /ɪkˈstriːm/
fact (n) /fækt/
figure (n) /ˈfɪɡə(r)/
grow (v) /ɡrəʊ/
location (n) /ləʊˈkeɪʃn/
long (adj) /lɒŋ/
size (n) /saɪz/
state (n) /steɪt/
time zone (n) /ˈtaɪm ˌzəʊn/
total (n) /ˈtəʊtl/

Unit 7

ball game (n) /ˈbɔːl ˌɡeɪm/
baseball (n) /ˈbeɪsbɔːl/
break (n) /breɪk/
Caribbean (n) /ˌkærəˈbiːən/
Latin America (n) /ˌlætɪn əˈmerɪkə/
national anthem (n) /ˌnæʃnəl ˈænθəm/
professional (adj) /prəˈfeʃənl/
relaxed (adj) /rɪˈlækst/
sociable (adj) /ˈsəʊʃəbl/
tea (n) /tiː/

Unit 8

accident (n) /ˈæksɪdənt/
bullet-proof vest (n) /ˌbʊlɪt ˌpruːf ˈvest/
community (n) /kəˈmjuːnəti/
crime (n) /kraɪm/
emergency call (n) /ɪˈmɜːdʒənsi kɔːl/
experienced (adj) /ɪkˈspɪəriənst/
fitness test (n) /ˈfɪtnəs ˌtest/
gun (n) /ɡʌn/
interview (n) /ˈɪntəvjuː/
investigate (v) /ɪnˈvestɪɡeɪt/
join (v) /dʒɔɪn/
local (adj) /ˈləʊkl/
missing person (n) /ˌmɪsɪŋ ˈpɜːsn/
police station (n) /pəˈliːs ˌsteɪʃn/
prepare (v) /prɪˈpeə(r)/
reduce (v) /rɪˈdjuːs/
respond (v) /rɪˈspɒnd/
robbery (n) /ˈrɒbəri/

Starter unit

Asking about families
Have you got any brothers and sisters?
What's your father's name?
Have you got a favourite uncle or aunt?
Where's your mother from?
How old is your grandfather?

Talking about schoolwork
Have we got maths homework today?
When's the geography exam?
Can I look at your history notes?
Who's your ICT teacher?
What time's the next English class?

Unit 1

Asking for and giving opinions
What do you reckon?
Don't you like it?
I can't stand … .
It's OK, I suppose.
Not much.
I'm not very keen on … .
I think it's really nice.

Expressing likes and dislikes
I'm really into … .
I'm (not) mad about … .
I'm a big fan of … .
I like/love/enjoy/prefer/hate … .
I don't mind … .
I'm not too bothered about … .

Unit 2

Finding things

Where's the … ?	It's next to … .
Where are the …?	They're in front of … .
Is there a …?	No, there isn't.
	Yes, there's one … .

Making requests and compromises

Can you (tidy your room), please?	I'll do it in (ten minutes).
	I'm busy at the moment.
Is it OK if I do it later?	I suppose so, but don't forget to do it!

Describing a place
It's a (modern flat), near the centre of town.
It's got three large bedrooms … .
You can see (the cathedral) from it.
There's a (DVD player) next to the (TV).
My favourite room is the (living room).
I like being in this room because … .

Unit 3

Talking about an experience

How was your weekend?	It was great.
What about you?	I … .
When did you last (play basketball)?	(A month) ago.
Was it good?	Yes, it was.

Linking events
First, … .
Then … .
At (+ time), … .
After that, … .
Finally, … .

Unit 4

Making and responding to suggestions

Why don't we (jump into the river)?	Yes, it looks (exciting).
Let's (cycle across Scotland).	Yes, that's a (good) idea.
	No, it's too (scary).
	No, that sounds (boring).

Expressing interest
Oh! That's amazing!
Really?
You're kidding!
Well done!
That's (very kind) of you.

Linking events
The (rescue) happened while (we were on holiday).
When they (reached the dog), they (put it in the boat).
After a few (minutes), we saw (the dog again).
As soon as they (saw the dog), they (swam out to it).

Unit 5

Expressing knowledge
I don't know much about … .
I know a lot about … .
I don't know anything about … .
I know a bit about … .

Choosing a present
He's into art.
Who's it by?
This one's better. I like it.
The other one's a bit (boring).

Writing a biography
She was born in (1775).
In total she (wrote six novels).
Her most famous (books) are … .
Her life changed when she … .

Unit 6

Making predictions
I reckon (that) ... .
I imagine (that) ... .
I bet (that) ... .
I'm pretty sure (that) ... .

Asking for and giving opinions
What about you?
I agree/disagree with you.
I think it'll ... .
Why's that?
Do you think ... ?
Let me think.

Expressing quantity
(More than) half of the people said ... .
Nobody / Everybody thinks that ... .
One or two people like ... .
Most / Some / A lot of us want to ... .

Unit 7

Making plans
What are you up to?
Are you doing anything this evening?
... if you're interested.
No, nothing special.
Shall I meet you outside?
It's on at ... (+ time)

Writing formal letters
Dear Sir or Madam,
I am writing to you because ... .
Please contact me ... .
I look forward to hearing from you.
Yours faithfully, ...

Unit 8

Reacting
Really?
I have!
Haven't you?
That's amazing!
So have I!
Neither have I!

Helping someone
What's wrong?
Are you OK?
How did that happen?
Maybe you need to ... .

Writing emails
How's it going?
Have you heard from (Amy)?
Guess what!
Write back soon.
See you, ...

Infinitive	Past simple	Past participle
be /biː, bɪ/	was /wɒz, wəz/, were /wɜː(r), wə(r)/	been /biːn/
become /bɪˈkʌm/	became /bɪˈkeɪm/	become /bɪˈkʌm/
begin /bɪˈgɪn/	began /bɪˈgæn/	begun /bɪˈgʌn/
bite /baɪt/	bit /bɪt/	bitten /ˈbɪtn/
break /breɪk/	broke /brəʊk/	broken /ˈbrəʊkən/
bring /brɪŋ/	brought /brɔːt/	brought /brɔːt/
build /bɪld/	built /bɪlt/	built /bɪlt/
burn /bɜːn/	burnt / burned /bɜːnt, bɜːnd/	burnt / burned /bɜːnt, bɜːnd/
buy /baɪ/	bought /bɔːt/	bought /bɔːt/
can /kæn/	could /kʊd/	
catch /kætʃ/	caught /kɔːt/	caught /kɔːt/
choose /tʃuːz/	chose /tʃəʊz/	chosen /ˈtʃəʊzn/
come /kʌm/	came /keɪm/	come /kʌm/
cut /kʌt/	cut /kʌt/	cut /kʌt/
do /duː/	did /dɪd/	done /dʌn/
drink /drɪŋk/	drank /dræŋk/	drunk /drʌŋk/
drive /draɪv/	drove /drəʊv/	driven /ˈdrɪvn/
eat /iːt/	ate /eɪt, et/	eaten /ˈiːtn/
fall /fɔːl/	fell /fel/	fallen /ˈfɔːlən/
find /faɪnd/	found /faʊnd/	found /faʊnd/
fly /flaɪ/	flew /fluː/	flown /fləʊn/
forget /fəˈget/	forgot /fəˈgɒt/	forgotten /fəˈgɒtn/
get /get/	got /gɒt/	got /gɒt/
get up /ˌget ˈʌp/	got up /ˌgɒt ˈʌp/	got up /ˌgɒt ˈʌp/
give /gɪv/	gave /geɪv/	given /ˈgɪvn/
go /gəʊ/	went /went/	gone /gɒn/
have /hæv/	had /hæd/	had /hæd/
hide /haɪd/	hid /hɪd/	hidden /ˈhɪdn/
hurt /hɜːt/	hurt /hɜːt/	hurt /hɜːt/
keep /kiːp/	kept /kept/	kept /kept/
know /nəʊ/	knew /njuː/	known /nəʊn/
learn /lɜːn/	learnt / learned /lɜːnt, lɜːnd/	learnt / learned /lɜːnt, lɜːnd/
leave /liːv/	left /left/	left /left/
lose /luːz/	lost /lɒst/	lost /lɒst/
make /meɪk/	made /meɪd/	made /meɪd/
meet /miːt/	met /met/	met /met/
put /pʊt/	put /pʊt/	put /pʊt/
read /riːd/	read /red/	read /red/
run /rʌn/	ran /ræn/	run /rʌn/
ride /raɪd/	rode /rəʊd/	ridden /ˈrɪdn/
say /seɪ/	said /sed/	said /sed/
see /siː/	saw /sɔː/	seen /siːn/
send /send/	sent /sent/	sent /sent/
sing /sɪŋ/	sang /sæŋ/	sung /sʌŋ/
sit /sɪt/	sat /sæt/	sat /sæt/
sleep /sliːp/	slept /slept/	slept /slept/
speak /spiːk/	spoke /spəʊk/	spoken /ˈspəʊkən/
spend /spend/	spent /spent/	spent /spent/
swim /swɪm/	swam /swæm/	swum /swʌm/
take /teɪk/	took /tʊk/	taken /ˈteɪkən/
teach /tiːtʃ/	taught /tɔːt/	taught /tɔːt/
tell /tel/	told /təʊld/	told /təʊld/
think /θɪŋk/	thought /θɔːt/	thought /θɔːt/
throw /θrəʊ/	threw /θruː/	thrown /θrəʊn/
understand /ˌʌndəˈstænd/	understood /ˌʌndəˈstʊd/	understood /ˌʌndəˈstʊd/
wear /weə(r)/	wore /wɔː(r)/	worn /wɔːn/
win /wɪn/	won /wʌn/	won /wʌn/
write /raɪt/	wrote /rəʊt/	written /ˈrɪtn/